WHAT YOU THINK
IS WHAT YOU GET

An Introductory Textbook
for the Study of the
Alexander Technique

Donald L. Weed, D.C.

ITM Publications

© 2004

Published by ITM Publications, PO Box 181, Bristol, BS99 7BH.

Previously published by:

1445 Publications
Lincoln, Nebraska

Gil Books
Bristol, Avon

In association with the ITM Teachers Association
Est. 1991 for Graduate and Post-Graduate Training in the F.M. Alexander Technique.

PO Box 181
Bristol BS99 7BH
United Kingdom
Tel: 0845 - 129 8395
Email: info@alexandertechnique-itm.org
Website: www.alexandertechnique-itm.org

A catalogue record of this book is available from the British Library.

ISBN 0-9548996-0-1

Cover design and layout by Peter Ruhrberg.

Printed and bound in the UK by Short Run Press, Exeter, Devon.

For everyone who will do the work

FM really discovered quite a different way of thinking.

– Marjory Barlow

The whole of it is a mental achievement, not a physical thing at all.

– Sir George Trevelyan

"You think that the Alexander Technique is a physical thing;
I can tell you that it is the most mental thing
that has ever been discovered."

– F.M. Alexander

ACKNOWLEDGEMENTS

The writing of a book is always a group project, no matter how lonely the process may seem to be.

There have been many people who have made major contributions to this book.

Marjorie Barstow and Frank Pierce Jones are mainly responsible for the training I have had. While the information I received in class time was priceless, I learned as much or more just by being able to be around such wonderful people. Without their help and friendship, I may never have gotten well, let alone become a teacher.

Sidney Friedman was the person most responsible for the development of the *Basic Principles* course. If he had not given me the opportunity to work in classes as a student teacher at Washington University, I would never have gained enough confidence early in my career to keep challenging myself to become a better teacher More importantly, without providing me with students who had to do homework to pass my courses, I might never have found out how valuable nineteenth-century-seeming educational techniques would be in learning this revolutionary, new work. Most importantly, he had the confidence in me to go along with all of my "improvements" in teaching, even when I am sure they didn't make sense to him. Thank you, Sid.

I am also very grateful to my colleagues at The Performance School. They let me bring the Basic Principles program into the school's curriculum, even though there were some strong reservations. Without the opportunity to teach the class in a longer format, with little or no experiential work, the course could never have evolved into its present form. Without the stimuli provided by our common vision, projects, and efforts, I might never have had the chance to find out what I really believe is the basis for standards of knowledge in this work.

My proofreaders, Heather Kroll, Kevin Ruddell, and Peter Lewis, are to be congratulated for having struggled their way through bits and pieces of early manuscript, and thanked for having provided me with the clues and keys I needed to learn how to make my writing a little more comprehensible on a first reading.

Karen is to be thanked, by all of us, for keeping the office and apartment running through Hell and High Water Music.

Lesley is to be thanked for teaching me more about possibilities, and reminding me that "not being allowed" was just a nightmare from my past.

And all of my students, old and new, are to be thanked for teaching me most of what I know, now, and in the future.

D.W.

ACKNOWLEDGEMENTS
FOR THE THIRD EDITION

MANY, MANY PEOPLE are responsible for the changes that appear in this edition and all deserve to be thanked.

The most obvious resources for change are all of the students that I have had in my experiential classes whose questions and experiences have either confirmed what I previously wrote or showed me where I was in error. In addition, I would like to thank all of the people who have participated in the four completed teacher-training courses as well as the students on my two current training courses. In their own way, they have given me the opportunity to fine-tune and simplify the many ideas that I wanted to present more clearly. Also, there have been many readers who have been kind enough to read the book and then contacted me either to praise the book or to take me to task for writing silly things. John Gil has once again provided the practical steps and impetus that I often lack. The ITM would not exist without his efforts and contributions. Emma Jarrett, Tracy Gil, Estella Cauldwell, Simon Gore, Tony Taylor, Linda Rosenberg, Barbara Warburg, and Veronica Pollard in England and Lesley Stephenson, Patricia Bollag, Ulf Tölle, Irma Hesz, Anke Leppke, Regina Neuenhausen, and Stefan and Anke Welsch on the continent have provided support and structure to my many projects over the years. My proof readers – especially Estella Cauldwell, Emma Jarrett, and Lynne Cartilidge – have saved me from myself and my punctuation many times and provided encouragement and support when they were often needed. Three additional people, though, are particularly deserving of special praise and thanks with regard to this project.

First of all, by taking over so much of the responsibility for representing the ITM in the voluntary self-regulation process, Richard Cauldwell has not only served the profession as a whole, but has freed up much time and energy for me to put into other projects such as this book. Secondly, Tim Kjeldsen, in addition to doing such a marvelous job in providing leadership during the transition of the current ITM Teacher's Association into its future form, presented me with more than twenty pages of perceptive and challenging notes and corrections which required another three months of revision to work through and incorporate into the text. Lastly, as with everything he does, Peter Ruhrberg, as the designer of this book, gave to this project a much higher standard of precision and accuracy with respect to details and formatting than it ever would have had if it had only been up to me.

Thank you one and all.

TABLE OF CONTENTS

PREFACE TO THE THIRD EDITION

IT HAS NOW BEEN more than fifteen years since I first began to write this book. I am very pleased by how well most of what I have written has stood the test of time. The 2nd edition of the book followed closely after the 1st edition because my colleagues at the time told me that they wanted more help with some of the concepts I was putting forth. After I had done that, though, I decided that I would let the 2nd edition stand as it was until such time as the need for making changes had become unavoidable.

I discovered in the last few years that I had stopped recommending the book as much as I once had. I decided that this was because I had become dissatisfied with some of the things I had written and with the ways some people were putting my ideas into action. A gap had occurred between the way I had taught these ideas then and the way I would teach them now, so I took advantage of the selling out of the most recent copies of the 2nd edition to act as a catalyst for making the new changes that I desired.

Overall, I am glad that I waited. Alexander's work is so subtle, and understanding it takes so long, that it took me until I had been teaching for nearly fifteen years before I felt I was ready to even try to write a first book. I am not at all surprised that it has taken an additional fifteen years to make the changes I am making today. After all, Alexander waited until he had been teaching for more than ten years before he wrote his first book, and there were at least nine years between each completely new one. In this edition, the changes I have made are of two kinds.

First of all, there has been an attempt on my part to simplify what I wrote earlier. This seemed to put me in conflict between two opposing tasks.

I was torn between preserving a teaching document that reflected how I was teaching at an earlier time and re-writing the material in order to teach it in the best way possible in the light of what I have since learned. While I probably wouldn't teach this material in this way ever again, what I taught then and how I taught it is still extremely important, foundational information. Since the late eighties, however, I have been learning how to present Alexander's work in a simpler, less demanding way. Consequently, the earlier approach no longer fits my teaching personality as once it did.

I also began to recognize that the book contains a practical introduction to most of the relevant material from the first year of my current teacher-training course. Throughout the book, but in the first two sections particularly, many of the key practical concepts and tools of the Interactive Teaching Method are presented. The third section summarizes the major principles for understanding the mechanics of how movement occurs as it is taught in the training course's anatomy and physiology module. The fourth and fifth sections discuss a paradigm for both the occurrence and persistence of habitual movement behavior and give a fairly detailed description of the key elements of Alexander's actual technique. Seeing the book in this way, I was led to the conclusion that mastery of the content would give readers practically everything they would need to change their lives significantly and constructively. Having reached that conclusion, the conflict between preservation and revision disappeared because I realized that, if all of these things were true, readers deserved to receive this information in the best possible way that I can present it.

So I decided to update the approach and make the necessary changes in content while keeping the book as close to its original format as possible. To accomplish this, I approached the text as if it were a rough draft I was working on today. As a result, information has been added and dropped. Sequences of clauses have sometimes been changed (e.g. in "The Rules of the Game", the sequence of clauses was changed at the cost of historical accuracy in order to make a clearer teaching point – a reversal of the decision I had made in 1989). The chapter "You Could Look It Up" was eliminated because, upon reflection, it seemed more like a free-standing essay than a chapter in a longer piece and the chapter on "Genuine Trust" was restored to its rightful place as one of the five key mental disciplines.[1]

I have also chosen to reflect the current focus in my teaching, that of approaching Alexander's work as a series of mental discipline to be mastered. This change in focus represents the second kind of changes in this edition.

The dominant role of the mental aspect of Alexander's work has always been a distinguishing characteristic of the Interactive Teaching Method. Although the importance of the mental discipline paradigm was part of the first two editions – after all, Alexander said that his work was "the most mental thing that has ever been discovered"[2] – the importance of mental discipline and its mastery has been clarified and strengthened throughout the whole of this edition of the book.

The one exception to this general policy of wholesale change is the appendix essay "For a Darn Good Reason". Although I have made some changes, particularly in the footnotes, I have tried to stay away from making many changes in the text. This document reflects not only a particular teaching stance and a historical point of view, but also the political circumstances and opinions that

---

[1] As a punctuation note, square brackets will be used to denote non-controversial changes made in quotations and parentheses will be used throughout in cases of authorial interjection, or in cases where the introduction of clauses and substitutions is either not so clear or disputed.

[2] Carrington, Walter, ed. Sontag, Jerry, *Thinking Aloud*. Mornum Time Press, San Francisco, 1994, p. 19.

surrounded the successful attempt by some people to exclude teachers trained by Marjorie Barstow from full participation in the North American affiliated society. Careful reading of the text will show that the issues facing the self-regulation process in our profession in the United Kingdom today are nearly the same as those dealt with in the States nearly twenty years ago (although one can now be more optimistic about a more positive outcome.)

The biggest change in this edition, however, is the elimination of the chapter entitled, "The Five Part Plan". The elimination of this chapter represents not just a process of simplification, but a complete change in policy with respect to what the ITM believes is important in this work and how the work is to be learned and practiced. Although this topic will be treated more completely in Volume II of the *Alexander Commentaries* entitled *The Evolution of a Technique,* I believe a simple explanation of why I dropped this chapter is warranted.

* * * * *

I first began writing Volume II of *The Alexander Commentaries* in 1992. The due date for completion of that text has come and gone many, many times. One of my early reasons for postponing the writing of that book was to avoid writing the *Commentaries* out of sequence. It seemed to me that it would be hard to know how to write Volume II if I hadn't written Volume I first. Since that time, the demands of creating and running the ITM teacher-training courses and all of the activities related to these courses have often kept me from my writing desk. But the real driving force behind not completing Volume II earlier was the simple fact that for many years I did not know how the book would end. For all of those years, I couldn't reach any certainty about Alexander's intent in the last few pages of his chapter and I didn't believe that I really understood enough about what was going on in those pages to publish a definitive commentary.

Today, most Alexander people know about the sequence of five steps that Alexander describes at the end of his chapter "Evolution of a Technique". Back in the eighties when I first wrote this book, though, this sequence was less well known, or at least less well talked about. The idea of giving these steps the name "Five Part Plan" came (as almost everything does in my work) from what I believed Alexander had written when he wrote that he must "at all costs work out some plan by which ... [his] instinctive reaction to the stimulus to gain [his] end *remained inhibited*, while [he] projected in their sequence the directions for the employment of the new use at the critical moment of gaining that end."[3]

That seemed pretty clear to me. He needed a plan to make sure that he kept his instinctive reaction inhibited while he continued to project his directions as he went into activity. The plan he devised had five steps. Easy. Call it the "Five Part Plan". It seemed to me that in this five-step procedure Alexander had left for

---

[3] Alexander, F.M., *The Use of the Self.* Gollancz, London, 1985, p. 45.

us a detailed blueprint for what to do to learn his technique and how to do it. I practiced this plan diligently. I even published a whole chapter in the book to make this very point. In fact, nowadays, I increasingly see this same idea – that the "Five Part Plan" is an important part of Alexander's technique – being put forward in print and in practice by other members of the Alexander community. Great stuff!

There is just one small problem with this approach: the ellipsis.

As it turns out, what I got out of that sentence – what I wrote above – isn't true. It's not what Alexander meant at all!

One "edits" Alexander at one's own peril and all too often the words that people choose to omit turn out to be significant. In this case, my editing made the sentence read as though the task, the purpose of this five-step procedure, was to ensure that Alexander's instinctive reaction remained inhibited as he went into activity. When one looks at the complete sentence, however, one sees that Alexander actually wrote that he must "at all costs work out some plan BY WHICH TO OBTAIN CONCRETE PROOF THAT[4] [his] instinctive reaction ... *remained inhibited.*"[5] As you can see, I got the transaction of the sentence completely wrong!

According to Alexander's complete sentence, the task of his five-step procedure was *not* to give himself a process by which to sustain inhibition of his instinctive reaction, but to give himself *a process by which to obtain proof* that his instinctive reaction had been inhibited and remained inhibited *by means of those described in the steps that made up his process of proof!* In other words, he wrote that he must work out a plan to prove that his instinctive reaction had been inhibited by means of the techniques he had described earlier in the chapter – the processes I have called the mental disciplines – the processes that make up Alexander 's actual Technique. The five-step plan Alexander described in the last pages of this chapter was not the technique itself, but only a way to check up, to prove, to see if his actual Technique had worked.

In my own defense, when I wrote the 2nd edition I was already questioning the proposition that this "Five Part Plan" was Alexander's intended technique for changing the use of himself in activity or even a part of that technique. In my classes, I had already begun to introduce this concept as the "Five Part Proof" rather than the "Five Part Plan". But I did not yet have sufficient understanding or conviction to make these changes in the 2nd edition. Consequently, although I altered some parts of the chapter back then in an attempt to downplay the power and importance of this sequence of steps, I was repeatedly faced with people who were asking me questions about how to "practice" the "Five Part Plan" as if it were one of the mental disciplines we had to learn in order to "do" the Alex-

---

[4]   My emphasis.

[5]   *ibid.*, p. 45.

ander technique. When I asked them why they thought this was so, they told me, "Because you said it was!"

In the end, I stopped recommending *What You Think Is What You Get* as much as I once had because I was tired of misleading people on this point. Over time, answering questions about this chapter had become increasingly hard for me to do. Watching people sitting quietly while occasionally lifting their hand had become more than I could bear. At the same time, I recognized that there was so much value in the rest of the book, that I became concerned that I may be penalizing people by not giving them sufficient encouragement to read the book in spite of the shortcomings of this one section.

I therefore welcome the opportunity to remove this chapter in this new edition. Others may continue to chose to pursue that sequence of five steps as if that was the way to "do" Alexander's technique, but they will no longer be able to blame me for telling them to.

*   *   *   *   *

Much has happened since this book was first published. Marjorie passed away. I put out a call for a new approach to teaching this work and training teachers, and when there wasn't a sufficiently large response in America, I moved to Europe. Here I have happily found and worked with a large number of people interested in learning Alexander's work in this particular way. Since 1993, more than a hundred people have gone through the Interactive Teaching Method's teacher-training courses and, in the fall, we expect another sixty or more to join us on our journey.

I hope that this new edition of *What You Think Is What You Get* will prove helpful to all students of Alexander and his work.

I hope that this book will help you reach your dreams.

Don Weed
Zurich
June 2003

AN OPEN LETTER
FROM MARJORIE BARSTOW

Dear Don,

What a great, great book you have created! It is just what the Alexander Technique world needs – yes, yes, yes!

I am sitting here at the dining room table, thinking of you, and hoping that many people are reading your book. *What You Think Is What You Get.* How true that is!

As I think back over the twenty years plus since you first came to me for lessons, and I remember how you were when you began and how you are now, I laugh a lot. I am very proud of all of the changes you have made, and very proud to have had a part in your making them. And now, you have handed me your very own book, ready for me and everyone else to read.

I consider it a great privilege to be asked by you to add a few words to your second edition. However, now as I start, I can see what a great task it will be. The things you have written in your book are so good, they are disturbing.

You call your book a textbook, and so it is. But, it is a different kind of textbook, because it is on a different subject: the Alexander Technique. By writing a textbook, you have opened up another direction for the investigation of movement and the technique.

Every time I start to read your book, my thoughts slip back to those early days when there were only three books written. What you have done in your book is what F.M. did in his, but in a different way.

I know that there will be people who will not like what you have done or who will think that the way you have approached the work is too different. There are many people like this who aren't willing to change, or who can't read or talk about something new and different without turning up their noses. These people can't see what I know, and I know that your book is a valuable tool that should be used by every student and teacher in this work.

When I see people react in this way, I want to shout to them, "Hey! Aren't you being just a little bit stubborn?" I want to say to them, "You can turn up your noses if you want to, but your noses are going to get scratched if you don't open your eyes!" Too often they just won't open their eyes and try something new. They'd rather stumble blindly along doing what they've always done, and believing that they are right.

After spending many hours working with your book, one of the things that pleases me the most is that it gives a fresh approach to F.M.'s "work." It is almost like fresh breezes flowing through the air. Your ideas and suggestions, like those breezes, are moving, and we need to keep up with them. How cleverly you have taken F.M. Alexander's discoveries and organized a moving structure around them, so that these discoveries can be better understood and used. Every thought you have written is so well explained, and then put to practical use. Your ideas are open and flowing – ready for action, and more action.

Now, as I read page after page, I begin to realize how much more I have yet to learn about that which I thought I already knew. The way you have opened my seeing! As I read your book, and think about the things you have written, and try them out for myself, I notice more and more that my own eyes are getting brighter and better. This is truly exciting for me.

Another thing which pleases me about your book is how timely it is. Just as there seems to be a growing demand for teachers, here comes your book, not only to help all of the new students, but to guide the new, young teachers as well.

A few weeks ago, I gave a workshop. I was surprised and delighted at the number of students who had copies of your book. Because they were reading your book, they were thing differently, and asking better questions. I do not think the workshop would have gone as well if there had not been so many students who had read your book. I do think that all of my workshops would go better if all of my students would read it.

Thank you for writing *What You Think Is What You Get*. As students of the F.M. Alexander Technique, I believe that we should all read your book again and again. If we did, we would all be better students and teachers, and, in time, we would come to appreciate the time and care and energy you have given in the creation of this book.

While writing this letter, I read a little poem on my desktop calendar which I thought was pretty good. I think it says what you and I are both trying to tell our students. With one little change, I'd like to share it with you:

> [Nature] has given us two ends
>> With a common link,
>
> With the one we sit
>> With the other we think.
>
> Success in life depends on
>> Which we choose,
>
> Heads you win,
>> Tails you lose.

Thank you once again for writing your book.

Cheerfully,
Marjorie L. Barstow
Lincoln, Nebraska

REVISED INTRODUCTORY

WHEN I first wrote *What You Think Is What You Get* over fifteen years ago, there were not many books available for the student of the Alexander Technique. Today this circumstance has changed, but my original reason for writing this book has not.

Most of the introductory books available on the Alexander Technique today are designed in some way or other to intrigue the general reader enough to pursue further information or to take lessons. As marketing material they serve a valuable purpose, but I believe that they fall far short of being of value to the serious student.

Although books like *Freedom to Change* by Frank Pierce Jones and all of Alexander's books are currently available, these books do not serve as a good introduction to the work because they are packed so full of information that they make better reference books than primers. Also they are not directly tied into the issues that come up in lesson experiences. For this reason, students sometimes experience difficulties linking up the information in these books with what they are going through in lessons.

What I believed was missing from the resources available was a good basic textbook that a student could read repeatedly to better understand the basic issues, experiences, and ideas involved in the Alexander Technique. What I believed the serious beginning student deserved was a textbook that presented Alexander's work in an informative way, which identified the major issues, which gave the student a good starting point for his study of this work, and yet, was sufficiently complex that one or two readings would not exhaust the value of the book.

What You Think Is What You Get is designed to fill the gap between the eye-catching introductory books presently available and the denser resources of Jones and Alexander. It is meant as a beginning point for a serious study of Alexander's work. All of the material in *What You Think Is What You Get* is based on the writings of F.M. Alexander. The format and the selection of material come from my more than thirty years of experience learning how to help students own the ideas in this work. Those who can master the material in this book will find that they have acquired what Alexander would have called a "satisfactory understanding of the theoretical side of his work,"[6] a condition Alexander required to be fulfilled before taking the student on to the further stages of teaching.

---

[6] Alexander, F.M., *The Universal Constant in Living*. Mouritz, London, 2000, p. 82.

People who are familiar with some of the various ways in which the "Alexander Technique" is taught and described may be surprised by the way material is presented here. Alexander's work is presented in this way because these approaches have proven valuable to my students. No previously held beliefs or perspectives or theoretical points of view were imposed on these ideas when they were introduced into the teaching process. In fact, I personally disagreed with many of the ideas presented here when I first encountered them. Time and time again, however, this approach helped make Alexander's work more accessible to my students and repeatedly served as the basis for a deeper understanding in my own experience. Consequently, I ask the reader experienced in the study of the work to suspend judgment about these new approaches, concepts, and terminology until he or she has spent sufficient time and energy to understand them as they are presented as well as the intent behind their presentation. Much of the material in this book is controversial and almost all of it is provocative. But this is almost certainly a good thing.

If, as Alexander claims, the major portion of a student's difficulty is to be attributed to the student's fixed (and preconceived) ideas and conceptions,[7] then one of my major tasks as a teacher must be to find some way to aid students in identifying and eliminating their mistaken ideas. Alexander says that in teaching, the teacher needs to deal with the student's preconceptions first, and "in dealing with them (the teacher) should not attempt to overlay them, but should eradicate them as far as possible"[8]. This eradication of students' erroneous preconceived ideas is my primary goal in almost everything I do as a teacher.

Many people, however, find this policy of constantly addressing these kinds of issues in class to be confrontational. If this process is, in fact, confrontational, then two things must be kept in mind. First of all, it is important to remember that what is confronted in class is always the ideas that people have, not the people themselves. More importantly, Alexander tells us that confrontation is necessary in the teaching of his work. He writes, "We all think and act ... in accordance with the peculiarities of our particular psycho-physical make-up"[9] except "when forced to do otherwise"[10]. "Forcing" people to do otherwise is one of the most important of Alexander's educational principles and it also determines much of the structure of my classes and the nature of my approach.

In my text-study classes, material is presented until some idea, issue, or comment sets off a reaction in one of the students. Then, whatever the point of

---

[7]   Alexander, F.M., *Constructive Conscious Control of the Individual.* STAT Books, London, 1997, p. 97.

[8]   Alexander, F.M., *Man's Supreme Inheritance.* Mouritz, London, 1996, p. 89.

[9]   Alexander, F.M., *Constructive Conscious Control of the Individual.* STAT Books, London, 1997, p. 108.

[10]   *ibid.,* p. 108.

contention may be, all of the energies of the teacher and the class are directed to the pursuit of this point until the problem is resolved or until no further questions can be easily asked or answered. As such, this teaching style is very dependent upon the interactions of each individual student with the material, with me, and with the other students.

For this reason, I prefer to call this teaching process the Interactive Teaching Method. One of the key tools of the Interactive Teaching Method is to engage the student actively in the discussion as a means for the student to examine and better understand his or her own ideas, thereby identifying limiting or harmful preconceptions for the purpose of eliminating them. Experience has shown that there is no better way to engage a student more fully than to threaten some precious, previously held, and often-unexamined concept or belief.

In the classroom, this lends a kind of provocative edge to many of the interactions. This inner (and often outer) turmoil creates an atmosphere that is occasionally uncomfortable, but one in which positions and beliefs are more clearly stated and examined. The purpose of these transactions is not to foist any particular position or concept on anyone. In fact, although some of my more outspoken critics are convinced that I "brainwash" my students, the most common complaint my students make is that I never tell them the right answers and that I hardly ever give them any answers at all. No, the purpose of these transactions is not to put forward any particular point of view but to create an arena in which everyone can actively re-examine their own points of view.

It has been a tremendous challenge trying to translate these classroom procedures into text. In the classroom, armed with the knowledge of the material and decades of experience working with thousands of students, I have learned how to tailor the proceedings to match the present needs of either the majority of students – or the neediest student – at any given time. Because all of these issues, problems, and difficulties are universal and because they are all issues that must be faced again and again in doing the work, focusing on the needs of any particular individual at any particular time almost always serves the needs of all of the students.

We have found that there is often a direct relationship between how clearly a position is stated and the ease with which the difficulties created by that position can be relieved. By dealing with each issue and idea as it is evoked, there can be a much more effective and lively identification of both the problems and their solutions. Over the years, the use of the Interactive Teaching Method has proven to accelerate the processes by which students gain both a theoretical command of this work and a capacity to do it easily on their own.

*   *   *   *   *

When I first wrote this book I worried about how I would bring this interactive form of teaching onto the page. I became quite concerned about how I was to

xxiv   Revised Introductory

direct the presentation to students who weren't there, or worse, how I was to present the material to every possible student at once. This concern grew to the point where it began to threaten the project, until I remembered one of the principles I teach in class.

Success education teachers say that if you are not making a lot of mistakes, then you are probably doing something wrong. One of the first tools to acquire in learning to experiment – a necessary aspect of learning Alexander's work – is a willingness to make mistakes, and a willingness to be wrong. This willingness to experiment and to be wrong is a very important starting point in the study of the Alexander Technique. Therefore, I decided to go ahead and write the book in the way that made the most sense to me, and accept it if I was wrong.

Another important technique that I teach with regard to making mistakes is to learn to make mistakes loudly. This is a concept which I learned singing in choruses. The choir directors always said to make your mistakes loudly. That way it would be so much easier to find where the mistakes were in order to correct them.

The same thing applies to making mistakes in learning this work. I teach that if you are going to make a mistake, make it big! Make it loud! There are no style points awarded in Alexander lessons. What is important is that students become more alert and clear about what they are thinking and how they are thinking it. By stating your ideas as clearly as possible, they are more available for examination and improvement. Therefore, I decided to make the statements in this book as loudly and as clearly as I can.

Another advantage of teaching live classes over writing things down in a book is that, in class, I am able to pick and choose which of the stories I will tell, which of the issues I will bring up, and in what order, to best suit the current needs of the students in the class. In bringing this classroom information into book form, I realized I would be limited to just a few stories, in just one sequence, which talk about only a few certain issues, without the benefit of any immediate feedback as a guide. I became concerned that, without a way to present this material to everyone at once, it would not be possible to present this material in a book format. But then I realized that there was a solution to this difficulty.

You see, in class, I consistently observe the intentions and implications of all that is said and done and relate these experiences meaningfully to past experiences and the ideas found in the work. While it is true that I was mostly alone while I wrote this, I could still "interact" with an idealized composite of all of my previous students. In that way, I could present issues and discuss ideas that reflected the most common needs my students have expressed, and answer the questions they have most commonly asked. In a sense, what I have done in writing this book is that I have told the story of how some mythical series of classes might have been taught to a mythical and ideal group of students.

Because I have decided to include in this book many, if not all, of the personalities and possibilities which might occur in class, it is unlikely that anyone will be able to read this book straight-through and not find at least some of it redundant, simplistic, bewildering, or just plain wrong-minded. My recommendation to you, the reader, is that you keep reading and re-reading it. As you change, so will the information in this book and your reaction to it as well.

More recently, the issues of inclusiveness and humor have come up in this regard. Students have often made the claim that I have left material out of the book – most particularly, the answers to their questions. They also claim that one of the main problems with the book is that I don't seem to have a sense of humor. I take it as a great compliment when I am told later that, as students learn more about themselves and the work, my book becomes funnier and more complete.

One last point. Because all of the different features of a live classroom presentation are being represented in print, it is unlikely that any single writing style can accommodate all of these transactions. The writing style, therefore, will be a mixture of formal and informal styles. Where possible, every effort has been made to make the material conform to common standards of good writing and gender neutrality.

Occasionally, a sentence structure or word choice that works well in person will resist translation into print. Similarly, the needs of conveying large amounts of precise information accurately and with the sense of simultaneity involved have sometimes created sentences of such length and awkward structure that they exceed even the length of Alexander's own sentences. According to my proofreaders, however, diligence and reading repetition will yield the full scope of the content of these longer sentences.

While I am forever and deeply indebted to my first teachers, Marjorie Barstow and Frank Pierce Jones, I have learned much from all who have taught me as well as from those who have worked with me as colleagues and those who have let me teach them.

Whatever success these efforts enjoy, the credit belongs to them.

Whatever faults are here to be found are mine alone.

OPENING THOUGHTS

Chapter 1

FIRST QUIZ

FIRST OF ALL, are there any questions?

If you have picked up this book, you should have a lot of them. Like, "What is the Alexander Technique? How does it work? How did it begin? How can it help me?"

Frank Jones began his book, *Freedom to Change,* with a similar question: "What can I do to be saved?" Although the question carries with it a plaintive tone reminiscent of the early seventies, the question it asks – and the questions it implies – still have validity for anyone who is seeking self-improvement.

I will assume that because you have read this far, you are interested in improving yourself and you are primarily interested in finding out if the Alexander Technique can help you. This last question may be the only question for which you will receive a quick and easy answer from me in this text.

Yes, the Alexander Technique can help you.

The Alexander Technique can help you in your everyday activities. It can help you in your specialized activities. It can help you walk. It can help you talk. It can help you do more, with greater success, in less time, using less energy.

But, there is a price.

You must think. You must discipline yourself. You must be willing to change.

Perhaps the willingness to change is the greatest price you will have to pay, because the First Law of the Alexander Technique is that people are willing to do anything to get better as long as they don't have to change.

*   *   *   *   *

Years ago when I was teaching at a university, a student dragged her boyfriend into one of my classes. She thought that since the work had done so much good for her, she wanted her boyfriend to enjoy the same special benefits. He didn't want to be there – and I never want to have anyone in any of my classes who doesn't want to be there – so we made a kind of mutual agreement that I would leave him alone, and he would try not to look too bored.

When it became apparent that his girlfriend wasn't going to give up in her insistence that he have a lesson, I asked him if he wanted to get it over with, or whether he wanted to walk out. He decided that it would cost him less in the long run to have the lesson than to put up with his girlfriend's harping about his not having it, so he sat down in the chair for a lesson.

First, I reviewed the ideas we had already talked about in class and explained the basics of the transaction that was about to take place when I put my hands on him. As soon as I put my hands on him, however, he was transformed! His slouched and hunched-over appearance disappeared. His face became more symmetrical and attractive. His voice lowered an octave. His eyes, previously dull and listless, were now vibrant, alive, and seeking. Even before I could ask him what he had noticed about himself, he had leaped to his feet, towered over me, shook my hand more forcefully than before, thanked me in a full and commanding voice that filled the room, and left.

He never came back to class.

This was in October.

Throughout the year, I kept seeing this fellow in the student newspaper. He was usually being singled out for some kind of honor or award. The one constant in all of the articles was about how he had been such a late bloomer, and how he had only recently begun to achieve the potential he had always demonstrated.

That May, right before graduation, I saw him walking across the quadrangle. His appearance and gait, if anything, had improved since last I saw him. He looked up, saw me, and having recognized me, ran across the quadrangle. I immodestly imagined that he was going to thank me for acting as the catalyst in the fabulous year he had been enjoying. When he reached me, though, he shook his fist in my face and shouted, "I've been trying to forget everything you taught me since I met you!"

Once I got over the shock of what he said, I asked him to explain why he was so angry.

He told me that ever since I had worked with him, he had continued to think about what I had said. As he continued to think about it, he continued to change. I asked him if he hadn't gotten better and improved and enjoyed great success. He said, "Yes, I have," but then, he added mournfully, in a way I will never forget, "But don't you see? I didn't want to change! I was happy the way I was!"

He taught me a very important lesson that day.

Sometimes people don't want to change.

Sometimes they are so content with themselves that they happily accept things as they are. The only reason why they show up in classes like mine is that they were either coerced, as this fellow was, or they have become secure in the belief that most classes that look like mine are unable to cause genuine change.

For many years after this incident, in almost every introductory class, I felt the obligation to warn people: "If you don't want to change, stay away from this work." As my friend Bradley Ehrlich put it, "The Alexander Technique is a catalyst for change," and a very powerful one at that. Therefore, if you do want to get better in yourself, and in everything you do, read on. If you don't want to change, stop now before it's too late.

*   *   *   *   *

If you've decided to go on (and I am glad that you have), I have a little task for you.

Take out a piece of paper and a pencil. Put your name and the date at the top of the page, because you are going to take a little quiz. It's very short. There is only one question. But, even though the quiz is very short, it is also very important.

When I do this in class, it accomplishes two things. First of all, it helps me learn more about the students in the class, their background, their training, and many of their most basic ideas. Secondly, and much more importantly, it provides a baseline against which each student's progress can be measured. That's the major reason why I want you to write out your answer to this quiz now. Later, after you've read this book and had some lessons in this work, I want you to go back, take the quiz again, and see how much you have learned.[11]

As I said, the quiz consists of only one question and the question I would like you to answer is, "What is the Alexander Technique?"

Be brief. Be concise. Be complete.

Answer the question as though someone that you care about has just asked you, and you want to answer as completely as possible, and in a way that will give them something of value while making them want to learn more.

Some of you will be so new to the work that you will believe that you don't know anything about it. If that's the case, then say so. Write it down. If you think you don't know much about the work, but you might know something, write it down. If you are a long-time student and you know so much about the work that it would take a long time to answer, take this opportunity to write down the best short definition you can. Make it something that is lively and informative, one that sings of the reasons for your own excitement about Alexander's discoveries. If you are a teacher, you answer this question often. See if you can find a new way to answer it that pleases you.

---

[11] I would also appreciate it if you would send to me a copy of the quiz you take now and the one you take after you have finished the book, as well as any other ideas you may have or papers you may write as you continue your study of this work. While I may not be able to respond personally to all of them, I learn so much from reading them.

Go ahead. Write out your answer now. I'll wait.

*   *   *   *   *

I have asked hundreds of people to take this first quiz. I never cease to be amazed by the wealth of information that it generates. Quite often, an answer will begin with an apology for how little the person knows, and then it will end with an eloquent response.

It really doesn't matter how you answer the question, though, because whatever answer you give is the correct answer. I asked you for your answer to the question. Whatever you wrote is your answer, so it must be the right answer for you at this time. About the only way you could get this quiz question wrong is if you wrote down something you didn't believe or copied somebody else's answer, and even then the only problem would be if you didn't give credit to that other person.

You see, I don't think there is a single right answer to this question because I don't think anyone really knows what the Alexander Technique is.

Chapter 2
THE DECISION GAME

THE QUICK thinking reader will have already figured out that I include myself in the group of people who don't know the single right answer to the question, "What is the Alexander Technique?" This is why I keep asking people. This is why my classes often sound more like a heated debate in the House of Commons than a poetry reading at high tea.

The best answer I have received so far to this question on a First Quiz was by Dr. Connie Amundson of Seattle, Washington. She wrote, "The Alexander Technique is the study of thinking in relation to movement." This definition is, in itself, controversial. For instance, I was recently asked by a very experienced teacher from another Alexander tradition, "What does study have to do with the Alexander Technique?" Similarly, another teacher asked, "What does thinking have to do with movement?" But, from the instant I heard this definition, I realized that someone had finally put into words the next great paradigm shift in understanding this work.

*   *   *   *   *

For years, those of us involved in the work have struggled to come up with a definition that encompasses all of Alexander's work. Alexander himself never gave us such a definition. In fact, he didn't even give us the name "Alexander Technique." He always referred to what he did as "the work." Once, in a defense of this practice of not naming his work, he wrote in a letter, "How can you name a thing that is so comprehensive?"[12]

One benefit that has come from asking students to write down answers to this quiz question is that there has been a synergistic relationship between the task of phrasing these definitions and making new discoveries in the classroom. Often a change in phrase will lead to an enlightening new experiment, and vice versa.

For instance, in the middle seventies, Marjorie Barstow asked me, "What can we do to get these people thinking?" By sharing her phrasing of the task in that manner and at that time, Marjorie confirmed for me the validity of the

---

[12] Maisel, Edward, ed., The *Resurrection of the Body*. Shambala Publications, Boston, p. viii.

direction I had already taken in my teaching and encouraged me to continue it. I was further inspired as she went on to say, "I'm convinced that the next great break-through in teaching will occur when we can finally get students to realize that it is their thinking that's important, not their movements or their feelings."[13] I had been actively working on how to get my students thinking, even before Marjorie had said this, but it took Dr. Amundson's answer on her First Quiz before it finally occurred to me that this should be the definitive starting point for learning this work.

*   *   *   *   *

Before Dr. Amundson's answer, my definitions had abounded with heads, bodies, relationships, movement, following, maintaining, ease, delicacy, improved performance, conscious control, and so forth. By defining the work in this new and different way, Dr. Amundson gave us a means with which to focus in on what is most important by placing emphasis on the need to study this work as well as an emphasis on the pivotal role played by the relationship of thought to movement.

In spite of the clarity of the phrase "the Alexander Technique is the study of thinking in relation to movement" (or perhaps because of it), there are many people who disagree with this idea. Many of the people who disagree will seem to the casual reader to be equally or better credentialed than Dr. Amundson or myself. What is someone to do when two or more experts disagree, particularly in a field where you have little knowledge or expertise yourself?[14]

---

[13] Interestingly, at approximately the same time in 1974, in one of his "lectures" during a training course session, Walter Carrington is quoted as saying, "Getting going, and the continuing to go ... is the real problem in the Alexander Technique, as in life. Now, one very good way, in fact the only real way, of getting people going is to make them think ... What's the best way of getting people to think? I'm afraid I don't know what the best way is." (Carrington, Walter, ed. Sontag, Jerry, *Thinking Aloud*. Mornum Time Press, San Francisco, 1994, p. 18.)

[14] Some people try to limit the phrase "Alexander Technique" to "just 'the way' that Alexander taught the work." To which I usually reply, "Since we have evidence that Alexander taught in a number of different ways, which 'way' did you have in mind when you limited your definition to 'the way' in which he taught?" If the person then says the 'way' he taught the people closest to him, then I point out that there is such diversity and disagreement among those people who were closest to him about what Alexander taught and how he taught it that it seems unlikely that any of them could really tell us how it was done.

Further, almost all of the Master Teachers (e.g., Barlow, Carrington, Macdonald, etc.) claim to have made improvements in Alexander's work after his death. It seems to me it would be hard for something to be improved and still remain the same. There-

This issue has come up most often for me with regard to health care. For instance, a patient might see me for a second opinion with regard to surgery when faced with making a choice between opposing recommendations. Similarly, all new parents who do any research on the subject are faced with a difficult decision about whether or not to have their babies vaccinated.

In fact, once one starts to think about "experts" and opinions, one quickly realizes that almost all of our decisions have to be made with the support of some experts and the condemnation of others. And the fact that large numbers of experts of great prestige hold a given position does not, by itself, make that position any more right than if their numbers or honors were smaller. For instance, I'm reasonably certain that most of the world's most prominent experts agreed that Columbus would sail off the edge of the world.

In his excellent book, *No Hidden Meanings,* Sheldon Kopp tells us that "all important decisions must be made on the basis of insufficient data." Often they must be made in the face of stiff opposition. All you can do as you approach any given decision is find out all that you can about the subject; or, if there is too much material, you can shop around in various sources until you mostly begin repeating what you already know, and then make a decision. All you can do is try to make your best guess at any given time. If you are right, terrific! If you are wrong, you can change.

I find as I work with people that many of them have a difficult time making decisions. They have become so accustomed to compromise and trying to make everything work all at once that the idea of systematically analyzing what they know to make a choice seems foreign to them, especially when the issues are complex and involved. At times likes these, I recommend that people use the Elephant Eater Technique.

James E. Tolleson, one of the foremost teachers of success education, asks anyone faced with a difficult and complex task, "How do you eat an elephant?" For many of us, this conjures up images too grotesque and bizarre to include in a family book, but the question remains, "How do you eat an elephant?"

The answer to this is really very simple.

You eat an elephant the same way you eat a chicken: one bite at a time.

For people faced with the problem of elephant-eating a difficult decision, like "How do I reconcile all of these diverse opinions about the Alexander

---

fore, the contention that the phrase "Alexander Technique" should be limited to "the way Alexander taught" is really not a tenable position. (A further development of this entire discussion can be found in Appendix A, "For a Darn Good Reason".)

Technique?" and "What is the Alexander Technique?" and "How should it be taught?" I recommend a tremendous tool for taking one bite at a time that I call "The Decision Game".

*   *   *   *   *

"The Decision Game" is a very simple game to play. What often causes people difficulty in their lives is their habit of mushing everything together in the way they think about things and thoughtlessly reaching premature compromises.[15] "The Decision Game" requires very different behavior indeed.

To play "The Decision Game", one first picks an issue or some aspect of that issue. Instead of trying to understand it better immediately, one then tries to state the issue in the two most opposite and illuminating ways possible. Then, using your left hand for one statement and your right hand for the opposite statement, point up and to the left side with your left hand as you say, "Between (position statement A) ..." then, point up and to the right side with your right hand and say, "... and its opposite (position statement B), which is more likely to be true, more likely to be what I want, more likely to help my career, etc.?"

This procedure will force you to take a stand on the essence of the decision you want to reach. For example, "Between cleaning my room, and going to a movie, which do I really want to do?" "Between asparagus and green beans, which do I want for dinner?" "Between Mozart and Salieri, who is the more enduring composer?" In fact, after a little practice, many people become so good at playing "The Decision Game", they can do it without using their hands. I recommend that even after you have built up your confidence playing the game, you use the gestures anyway when the decisions are more difficult. For those of you who teach, I recommend that you play "The Decision Game" out loud, using the gestures, when you are explaining something in class.[16]

---

[15] In the Basic Principles classes, we call this tendency to mush all of one's points and ideas together "The Dog Sled Theory." Often by merely teasing apart the various ideas that have been mushed together and then using consistency in logic and in the definitions of terms, students will find their own solutions to self-imposed problems.

[16] The real art involved in playing "The Decision Game" has to do with the way in which you phrase your choices. As you start to use this technique, there are three things to keep in mind. Firstly, you must search for the key issue involved. Secondly, you must make sure that your choices represent genuine choices or opposites. Finally, my recommendation is always to make your choices as colorful and humorous as possible. The more actively you involve your intellect and creativity by phrasing your choices in interesting ways, the more likely you are to break through into a new insight or decision.

The real value of "The Decision Game" to the Alexander Technique is that we can use it to identify some very basic issues, and find out where we stand on them. For instance, between (left hand) "We know what the Alexander Technique is," and (right hand) "We don't know what the Alexander Technique is," I have already declared for the second choice. The reason why I believe that "We don't know what the Alexander Technique is" is that although there are so many different answers given by so many different, trustworthy people. Before Dr. Amundson, though, nobody could give me a simple definition that I thought was both complete and satisfying.

*   *   *   *   *

When we know what something is, we can usually communicate what it is, or, at any rate, agree about what it is. For instance, most of us can agree on what a tomato is. Or what music is, though we may argue forever about what good music is or even if there is such a thing as "good" music. (For instance, is "good music" music that is well behaved? And if it is, then weren't the stodgy musicologists right every time they said that a new pioneer like Mozart or Wagner wrote bad music because it broke all of the rules?)

If one were to listen to all of the definitions available for the "Alexander Technique," these mutually exclusive diversities would quickly eliminate any possible hope of agreement. More to the point, for every time we could find an expert who was watching what a teacher was doing in a lesson who would say, "That's the Alexander Technique," I can probably produce at least one other "expert" who would say, "No, it is not!"

Even after one has successfully played "The Decision Game", it may be apparent that there is still not sufficient information to reach a final conclusion. When this happens, it is often helpful to use another ITM technique called "Asking the Next Question". When a question in "The Decision Game" remains largely unresolved, it is often helpful to see if it is possible to formulate another question that might explain the first question more clearly. Once formulated, this second question would be, of course, the "Next Question".

One of the best strategies for asking these "Next Questions" is to work your way backwards as far as you can to the underlying premises and assumptions behind any circumstance or point of view. Then, you can look at the first question once more to see if any further "Next Questions" need to be asked.

Often it requires asking very many "Next Questions" before the logjam of indecision with regard to the initial question can be answered. Sometimes even when you have searched as far back as is seemingly possible; the initial question will remain unresolved. Almost always though, any stubborn question will yield to the answers gleaned from the appropriate "Next Questions".

In the case of the issue we have at hand – whether or not anyone knows what the Alexander Technique is – a valuable "Next Question" to ask might be whether or not Alexander's work is finished or complete or perfected. If, for instance, you decide that the work is finished, then it would be possible for you to hold the position that the Alexander Technique is completely definable and therefore one can know what it is. If, on the other hand, you think as I do, that Alexander's work and the technique for teaching that work is not finished but is rather constantly evolving in significant ways, then it would be difficult to define the work in any complete or final way and you would probably have to concede that you don't know what the Alexander Technique is or will be.

For me, I don't think it is possible to know fully, finally, once and for all, what anything is if it has the possibility of being changed dramatically with just a change in thought. Further, if you believe as I do, you would have to believe that not only is the work unfinished, but that we all have the duty, in fact, the obligation, to contribute to the work as we learn it.

This is where the genuine excitement in this work lies for me. Not only do I get the advantage of learning information and procedures that have demonstrated to me clear and growing benefits, but everything that I can contribute to the work will be a significant contribution that will benefit others as well.

This is what I tell all of my students, too. Anything that they contribute – anything that you contribute – to this new, evolving, and unfinished work, will be a significant contribution that will help others as much as it helps yourself.

*   *   *   *   *

Sometimes even "Asking the Next Question" will not bring clearly into focus the solution to the initial question. At that point, the practiced decisionist engages in a discipline called "Scoring".

"Scoring" in "The Decision Game" is accomplished by making the same distinctions as before ("Between A and B"), and then, while thinking of the two choices, you decide on one or the other by seeing towards which side of the decision you are leaning. In other words, you decide where you would "score" your opinion with respect to the midline between the two extremes. Then, because the rules of the game state that the midline – the exact mid-point between the two decisions – behaves as though it were an infinitely high, infinitely steep mountain with perfectly smooth frictionless sides, whichever side you favored when you scored your opinion becomes the position that you hold.

Even if you do not or cannot believe that this newly held position is the true position, you carry on "AS IF" it were. By acting on this "AS IF" principle, one of two eventual outcomes will result. Either the action and the decisions engendered by the "AS IF" decisions you have made will subsequently be proven false – or they won't. In those cases where your adopted position has proven false, you can re-play "The Decision Game" with improved information and benefit. In those cases where your "AS IF" decision has proven true (or failed to prove false), you have taken a course of action that so far has proven to be of benefit.

In other words, "Scoring" prevents "Fence Sitter's Folly",[17] the process of keeping yourself mired in inaction while you can't make up your mind. By scoring your decision, and accepting the strong statement of the position you favor, you can now act based on one of the positions or the other.

The best thing that could happen if you act "AS IF" one of the choices was right is that the choice was right, you did act, and you accomplished your goal. The worst that can happen if you act "AS IF" one of the choices was right is that you could be wrong. If you are wrong, you can then learn from your mistakes. You can learn how you were wrong, how to institute new and better procedures and thereby improve your chances of reaching your goal the next time.

In fact, usually, the only procedure you could follow which could genuinely be called a bad procedure would be if you sat around doing nothing because you couldn't make up your mind which choice was right. Once you begin sitting around in this way, it is more likely than not that you will continue to sit around in this way and never reach your goal. Except when it does, almost nothing good ever comes from just sitting around.

---

[17] "Fence Sitter's Folly" is the name I give to the policy of remaining compromised in the middle of a decision. After having made a decision about which way you really believe an issue should be decided, it would be sheer folly to remain "sitting on the fence" and fail to take action on that issue. Even when you haven't made a decision about what you want to do, "sitting on a fence" rarely advances you because it limits your capacity to generate more information. Limiting your capacity to generate more information is a problem because with more information, troubling choices often become easier.

By focusing on small manageable steps with clear, definite decisions, you can begin to form a course of action that will bring you what you want. Bite by bite, decision by decision, issue by issue, what you really think about something and what you want to do about it will become increasingly clear. As your goals and needs become clearer, it will become easier to create strategies for reaching them. As your strategies improve, your rate of success in reaching your goals will improve as well.

*　　　　*　　　　*　　　　*　　　　*

So far, we have used "The Decision Game" to identify two important issues with regard to how one sees the Alexander Technique. The answers to these questions are basic and in large part will determine almost every other answer that you make about the work. Right now, maybe you should take some time to write out your own answers to these two questions as a way to see where you stand.

First of all, between "We do know what the Alexander Technique is," and "We don't know what the Alexander Technique is," which statement do you think is more likely true? Where would you score yourself on this issue? Secondly, between "Is Alexander's work finished, complete, and whole," or "Is Alexander's work still unfinished and evolving," which do you believe is more likely true?

In case you weren't sure, when I wrote out my answers just now, I decided to behave "AS IF" this work was unfinished and evolving. Consequently, even if I knew everything there was to know about what the work is now – and I don't – I still couldn't say I know what the work actually is because I do not know what it will become.

These are my decisions today on these two issues. Everything that I decide and write about in this book from this point onward will reflect these decisions.

For right now, it doesn't matter whether you agree with me or not on these issues (or any other issue for that matter). The important thing is that we are both willing to take a stand, to share our ideas with one another, and be willing to change to the point of view that makes the most sense, no matter whose point of view it originally was. Many times during this book, and in all of my other books, we will be playing "The Decision Game". I recommend that you try it out in everything that you do. I think you will find it of great value.

*　　　　*　　　　*　　　　*　　　　*

Since you had to answer the first quiz in the last chapter, it seems only fair that I should share with you my answer to the First Quiz. In fact, I'll not only share the answer I wrote in the 2nd edition, but I will share a brand new answer with you today. I don't know how many times my answer to this question has changed so far nor can I guess how many times it will change in the future. That doesn't matter. Every time I change my answer, it means that I've learned something in between. Now that you have some more background, I think you'll see the sources of some of my definition. Some of it may still be unfamiliar or difficult to agree with, but we will talk about all of the ideas in these definitions before we are done.

Don Weed
August 20, 1989

First Quiz

The Alexander Technique is an as yet unfinished and constantly evolving investigation of the relationship between thought and movement behavior, and how the retraining of the conscious mind can be used by individuals to bring about continuous and constructive changes in the quality and efficiency of their general standard level of performance in all of their activities.

Don Weed
February 15, 2003

First Quiz

The Alexander Technique is an as yet unfinished and constantly evolving investigation and study of the causal relationship between thinking and movement and how we can learn to discipline our thinking to take advantage of certain principles and physiologic truths so that we can raise our standard level of general performance in all of our activities and more easily realize much more of our latent potentialities in order to design our lives and reach our dreams.

Chapter 3

"YOU CAN DO WHAT I DO"

ONE OF THE MOST important things that F.M. Alexander ever said is something which he is reported to have been quite fond of saying: "You can do what I do, if you will do what I did." Sadly, this phrase has been both dreaded and ignored ever since he said it.

For those people in search of the secret of the Alexander Technique, this is the ultimate bad news. This means that, just as there is no secret to success, there is no secret to the Alexander Technique. There is only work.

The people looking for the secret to the Alexander Technique are looking for a short cut. They are looking for a way to get the benefits of the work without having to earn them. These are the people most likely to ask, "How can I do the Alexander Technique?" They are also the people that, when you tell them how to "do it", will be sure that you are wrong or withholding something when you tell them.

To others, this phrase of Alexander's represents the clearest, most concise game plan for learning his work. One only needs to do what Alexander did. Too often, though, these people choose to limit their concept of what Alexander did to a certain manner of posture and movement or to a certain pattern of repeated words or to a certain way of teaching using set procedures. But, Alexander did much more than that!

He observed himself in his manner of performing activities. He reflected upon these observations. He challenged his ideas with experiments.

Elsewhere I have written at greater length about the process of investigation which Alexander constantly employed during his discovery of his technique and which we will have to employ if we are going to do what Alexander did.[18] We can't just project his directions and let our necks be free, etc. We, too, will have to follow this same process of observation, postulation, experimentation, evaluation, and adaptation. We will have to be willing to look at anything and everything, including Alexander's own ideas, as he was willing to look at them: in a constructive but critical way. We will have to reason these ideas out and then work to prove or disprove them in a practical manner.

---

[18]   See Appendix A.

There is a tendency in many of us to see Alexander's work – or at least our understanding of it – as some unassailable writ. We often approach his ideas and writings as though the parts we understand and agree with are the parts that are accurate and true. They seem worthy of learning as is, and hence beyond investigation or proof. The other parts, the ones we don't understand or agree with, we tend to ignore, discount, apologize for, or "improve" as we read them or encounter them in practice. Once again, our primary desire seems to be to minimize the amount of time and effort spent in understanding the principles and concepts that comprise Alexander's work.

It's as though people still believe that, with enough lessons from a sufficiently skilled or venerated teacher, they won't have to bother with a careful and close examination of who they are and how they work.[19] They think they won't have to challenge their most basic ideas. They think they won't have to come to understand that what they do is not nearly so important as how they do it. They think they won't have to learn to replace their concepts of correction with concepts of prevention and reasoning. They still believe that they will not have to examine, evaluate, dismantle, and reconstruct their entire means of taking in information and formulating responses, but will still be able to acquire the benefits of Alexander's work.

And, unfortunately, to some limited and limiting degree, they can.

*   *   *   *   *

Because efficiency is a measure of the relative amounts of effort required to achieve a particular end, any change in the performance of a given activity that requires less effort for similar or better results would represent an improvement in efficiency. In my classes, I make a distinction between the three kinds of improvement in efficiency that are possible.

The three ways to improve efficiency in the performance of an activity are 1) to change the protocol, 2) to decrease the amount of wasted effort used in the performance of an already known protocol, or 3) to change the direction of the manner of use of the self in the performance of either a new or already known protocol. Both of the first two kinds of improvements are ways that are familiar

---

19 For example, in the book *The Alexander Technique As I See It*, Patrick Macdonald is quoted as saying, "As you can see, quite a lot of mental hard work is involved. Alexander spent hours, weeks, months, and years doing it. We are not Alexanders and, luckily for us, we are not called upon to go through all the drudgery that F.M. did. A skilled teacher, with his hands, (will give us what we need) without the pupil having to undertake more than a tithe [a tenth] of the mental discipline that Alexander had to use." (Rahula Press, Brighton, 1989, pp. 81-2.)

and available to everyone. As we shall see, only the third way is uniquely the province of the Alexander Technique.

A protocol can be thought of as the steps taken to perform an act. By evaluating the steps in a given protocol, sometimes a change in the order or nature of the steps taken will create a more efficient performance of that task. Sometimes the change in protocol can be external to the performer, like getting a different or better tool, or they can be internal to the performer, like deciding to change the sequence of actions taken. These kinds of changes are of value and are clearly part of Alexander's work, but they don't require any knowledge of Alexander's work to carry out. Therefore, they are not unique to the Alexander Technique.

What is also not unique to the Alexander Technique is improvement of efficiency by a decrease in effort. This is the kind of increase in efficiency which I call "doing the 'same thing less'". For instance, if someone performed an act with a distorted psycho-physical equilibrium and a great deal of strenuous effort, then a simple way to perform that act more efficiently and with greater comfort would be to perform it with the same psycho-physical disequilibrium in the performance of the act, as before, but with less effort. This, without question, would produce a more efficient, more pleasant feeling movement, and the degree of change might be significant, but it wouldn't really require knowledge of Alexander's discoveries to bring about and is actually more of the nature of fooling yourself than genuine change and improvement.

And yet, there are a number of practitioners who teach that in order to do what Alexander did all we "have to do" is move as he moved. They teach the mental rehearsing of phrases like "forward and up" and "back back" in combination with correct "kinesthetic experiences" as a kind of politically correct process while minimizing the training of their students' powers of intelligence. It is as though for these teachers "thinking" is merely a way of facilitating the all-important postural and movement behaviors associated with the work rather than the key to reaching the plane of conscious control from which improvement can be generated at will.[20]

It is as though by creating the physical, postural, movement-efficiency characteristics of the Technique, these teachers believed their students could work backwards through their "psycho-physical unities" to train their mental processes. But this approach cannot possibly work because, as we shall talk about later, it is not movement that creates thoughts, but rather thoughts that create movement. It is the training of a person's ability to think in a certain manner that lies at the heart of this work, not the ability to move or stand or sit in any par-

---

[20]   There were even groups of teachers in the late eighties who were into teaching their pupils about peripheral reflex facilitation and the proper way to sneeze.

ticular way.[21] Improving the relationship of one's head and body in activity without a corresponding retraining of one's thinking to alter the means of directing oneself to a more reasoning process is a hollow victory unworthy of being called the Alexander Technique.

*   *   *   *   *

What did Alexander do?

After discovering the misdirection of his efforts, Alexander looked into the manner in which he directed his efforts. And so must we. Alexander challenged his thoughts with reflective examination and then challenged them again. And so must we. He used practical experimentation to discover which of his ideas worked and which did not. And so must we.

We all have an obligation to pursue this work every day as if from the beginning because Alexander did just that, and this process of pursuing and experimenting with knowledge about himself and the workings of his mechanism became part of how he learned. It was part of "what he did."

I understand that there are some people who, out of respect I suppose, think of and/or teach Alexander's work as if it were whole and finished and needing to be preserved. As I said earlier, it is inconceivable to me that this could possibly be true. Everyone will have to decide for him- or herself whether they think Alexander's work represents some finished, whole, or "revealed" truth that must be cherished and preserved OR whether the work was just F.M.'s best shot at any given time to understand himself and the way he directed himself in activity. Are we going to "deify" Alexander and "mummify" our concepts of his procedures thereby making "off limits" for investigation his words and whatever of his procedures we have preserved, OR are we going to accept him as a brilliant, self-credentialed colleague who is going to assist us in our common goal of exploring his work?

To me the choice is clear.

It is often said that by giving someone a fish you make him or her dependent upon you. If you teach them how to fish, however, you will free them to feed themselves. Alexander didn't give us some sort of overly precious and delicate fish to eat unexamined. He taught us how to fish! He didn't leave us at the mercy

---

[21] In fact, Alexander tells us explicitly that in his work "the pupil is not taught to perform certain new exercises or to assume new postures for a given time each day ... but he is shown HOW he may at once check ... the faulty use of [his] mechanisms ..." (Alexander, F.M., *Constructive Conscious Control of the Individual*. STAT Books, London, 1997, p. 160.)

of his shortcomings or the limits of his knowledge and investigations through a dependence upon him or his representatives. He gave us the tools with which to do this work for ourselves.

But, in order to do this work, we will have to do what he did – not only in terms of the manner of our movement, but in the manner of our thinking as well.

Alexander also learned to teach the work, and he learned to write about the work. He took upon himself the added tasks and responsibilities of coming to know the work so well that he could communicate it to others. Perhaps we will also have to do these things to reach his level of understanding.

The determining factor in learning this work can't be the number of lessons a person has had: Alexander didn't have any, and A.R.[22] only had six. It can't be receiving proper kinesthetic information from a properly trained teacher because neither Alexander brother ever had anyone "put hands on" them while they were learning. It can't be simply the number of hours spent in a classroom because even well respected heads of training have admitted to me that "the occasional dud" has made it through their training programs.[23] It is not even the degree of aptitude or ability we bring to learning the process that is significant.

A man whom I consider to be one of the best teachers of Alexander's work had a tremendous difficulty in relating to students when he first began teaching because his coordination was so good to begin with that he couldn't understand why others didn't change as quickly as he. At the other end of the spectrum, my nickname in my first training class was "Old Stonehands"[24] and, on the basis of my natural aptitude, understanding, and condition, I was no one's favorite teaching partner and avoided at all costs. In fact, in 1991, during a class I was teach-

---

[22] Albert Redden Alexander (1874-1947) was F.M. Alexander's brother and the only other person that Alexander consistently had faith in as a teacher.

[23] Marjory Barlow puts it even more strongly: "Out of a training course come a range of people, some of whom won't teach at all, some of whom will be poor teachers, some adequate, and occasionally a superb one or two." (Barlow, Marjory, *An Examined Life in conversation with Trevor Allan Davies.* Mornum Time Press, Berkeley, 2002, p. 232.)

[24] I must confess that it amuses me to find that of all the controversial claims in this book, this is the claim that is most often disputed. It is flattering, I suppose, that my current students or even students who studied with me as early as the fall of 1974 say that I couldn't possibly have had hands that felt as bad as I claimed. It was reassuring for me, however, to watch one of my colleague's reaction when she heard someone challenge this assessment at the International Congress in Switzerland in 1991. She assured the objector that in 1972, when I began using my hands to work on her that "Old Stonehands" was not only accurate but probably a compliment.

ing at the International Congress of Teachers, Marjorie Barstow publicly confirmed that I was the worst beginning student she had ever had.[25]

All one needs to do to become accomplished in this work is to follow the procedures outlined here and in Alexander's books and in your teacher's classes. There are sufficient maps available for you to find your way if you will do the work. Like my first T'ai Ch'i instructor used to say, "Everybody can do it. Some a little slow. Some a little fast. But, everybody can do it!" You just have to do for yourself what Alexander did for himself.

"You can do what I do if you will do what I did."[26] It seems like such a simple phrase, but if we were to practice it to its greatest depth of meaning, we couldn't help but accomplish for ourselves at least the same degree of constructive conscious control that Alexander enjoyed.

---

[25] I've often wondered if my difficulties as a beginner in this work weren't somehow an advantage. Nothing came easily. I couldn't see anything. I couldn't feel anything in a lesson. I couldn't understand what most of my classmates were so excited about. From the beginning, I have had to work for everything I have achieved in this work and the tools that I acquired and refined along the way have served me and others well.

If there are one or more aspects about the practice or understanding of this work that concern you, the reader, because you don't get it or see it or feel it, put your concerns aside and just get busy. If I can go from where I was to where I am, and be where I am going, you can do anything. All that is required is that you do the work.

[26] Actually Marjory Barlow reminds us in several places that this is only a partial quotation. For example, in a summary about a master class which she taught in Zurich (Martin, Kevan A. C., "Marjory Barlow and Elizabeth Walker, 5 Day Masterclass Workshop, 1997, p. 1), the writer tells us, "One participant asked her where he could find the source of FM's statement that, 'You can do what I do if you do what I did.' She said she had heard it from FM himself, but that in the retelling the crucial ending was always left off: "... but none of you want anything mental!'" This is clearly further support for the ITM contention that Alexander's work is about mental discipline.

AN INTRODUCTORY LESSON

Chapter 4

ONE THOUGHT

WHEN I TEACH an introductory Alexander class, I always start by telling my students Dr. Amundson's definition of Mr. Alexander's work, that "the Alexander Technique is the study of thinking in relation to movement." After discussing this definition with them for a while, I then ask, "If the Alexander Technique is the study of thinking in relation to movement, then wouldn't it make sense to begin our study of the Alexander Technique with a thought?" After they say yes, I tell them the One Thought we use in the Interactive Teaching Method to begin our study of the Alexander Technique.

It's a simple thought and easily remembered. It articulates, among other things, a very important physiologic truth that we will spend much of the rest of the time in an introductory class investigating. I sometimes tell my students that if they remember nothing else from our first encounter together except this One Thought, then I will consider my efforts successful.

The One Thought that I want them to remember is this:

ONE THOUGHT:

> the poise of a person's head
> in relation with his or her body
> in movement
> is the key
> to freedom
> and ease of motion.

When it is written down and said out loud, it seems quite easy to understand and perhaps even obvious. But, it wasn't obvious to Alexander. This statement represents a combination of principles and discoveries that took him many years of experimentation to find.

When Alexander began his study, he was trying to solve a specific problem: throat troubles which threatened the loss of his voice during his dramatic recitals. He first tried the medical and vocal experts' solutions to his problems. When those solutions didn't work, he had to accept personal responsibility for being the cause of his own difficulties. To find his own solution, he had to train himself to observe his manner of using himself in the activities of ordinary speaking and reciting.

While doing this, he noticed that he had a tendency to do the same three things each time he began to speak: he would 1) pull his head back, 2) depress his larynx, and 3) gasp or suck air in through his mouth immediately before he began speaking.[27]

Once he had identified these three tendencies, he had to work out which of the three was controllable. He quickly found out that he could not directly control the depressing of his larynx or the sucking in of air prior to speaking. He did find, however, that the pulling back of his head was not only directly controllable, but that if he could control the pulling back of his head directly, this enabled him to prevent indirectly the other two faults from happening.

Then, through further experimentation, he came to see that these three tendencies were not only a misuse of the parts involved in vocal production, but that they also constituted a misuse of his entire mechanism. This misuse could be caused by idea-generated movements as simple as a distortion of the relationship of his head to his body in movement, or as subtle as his attempts to carry out faithfully a correction about how to stand given to him by a respected teacher.

This statement of the One Thought with which we begin our study of this work – though simple and easy to remember – distills years of brilliant investigation and reasoning by Alexander into an excellent starting point, and, as such, deserves further investigation itself.

*   *   *   *   *

<u>ONE THOUGHT</u>:

the poise of a person's head

People often wonder why I begin this statement with the word "poise."

There are many reasons.

First of all, I use "poise" because people are unfamiliar with it. It gets their attention. It lets people know that something new is being presented. The word "poise" demands their attention in a way that a familiar word would not. Secondly, it prevents people from deciding immediately that they already know what I am saying because my word choice introduces a sense of uncertainty. Most importantly, the major characteristic of the word "poise" which distinguishes it from "position" and "posture" is a sense of motion.

---

[27] Alexander, F. Matthias, *The Use of the Self.* Gollancz, London, 1985, p. 26. The succeeding claims come from the same section through page 30.

Obviously, "position" refers to placement rather than movement. For something to be in its position, it has to be in its place and stay there. In the case of movement behavior, a "position" would refer to the relative and static placement of body parts with respect to other body parts.

The word "posture" suggests a static state as well. Most people have a sense that there is a right "posture," a right way to stand or sit or be. Many can even recite a litany of appropriate directions for acquiring "good posture": "Chin in! Chest out! Shoulders back!" These people actually believe that if they could constantly maintain these optimum placements of their parts, they would have good posture – and that is a static concept.

One of the strengths of Mr. Alexander's work is that it recognizes that we are made to be in constant motion. More importantly, it is a fact that we ARE in constant motion, no matter what our usual concepts about motion imply. Even when we are "still," there is movement within us. There is breathing, of course, and heartbeats, but I mean more than this. There are constant shifts and adjustments of our body parts in relation to one another even when we don't think of ourselves as "moving."

The Alexander Technique is about many things and one of the most important is movement.

So, because the word "poise" is different, unfamiliar, and best implies motion, I use it when I state the One Thought with which we begin our study of Alexander's work.

*   *   *   *   *

ONE THOUGHT:

the poise of a person's head
in relation with his or her body

In the course of his lifework, Alexander made or articulated many discoveries about who we are and how we work. One of the most basic of these discoveries has to do with the importance of the relationship of one's head with one's body as the controlling factor in movement and coordination. This head/body relationship is basic, powerful, and occurs first in the sequencing of all movements. Alexander talks about the employment of this relationship as being the primary control of the manner of use in all activities.

As we study the Alexander Technique, we will have much to say about the nature and importance of this relationship. For now we will just remember that the first part of the first thought involved in the ITM study of the Alexander Technique has to do with the poise of one's head in relation to his or her body.

ONE THOUGHT:

the poise of a person's head
in relation with his or her body
in movement

It is important to remember that one of the major sources of confusion in this work (and in many other kinds of work, I suppose) is that we often use a single term in more than one way, with more than one meaning, within the same context, often within the same sentence. Further, we are not clear always about these multiple meanings or about the reasons why we made them. Even more often, we don't even realize that we made this kind of error in the first place.[28]

This, usually innocent, "carelessness" lends itself to criticisms by the "careless" of the limitations of language. Such criticisms provide them with even further absolution from an effort on their part to communicate more clearly. It is not my place or intent to suggest that language is not limited. Language is limited, but this kind of carelessness is not an example of the limitations of language but rather an example of the ways in which additional "limitations" can be created by the ways in which language is being used. My point here is to suggest that the real limitations in any area are often greatly augmented in practice by the "limitations" that the less than careful user of language is not inclined to perceive.

I have been told that in order to keep a circus elephant from wandering off, all that is required is to tie a rope around its leg that is similar to the ropes used to tie it up when it was younger. As a baby, the elephant "learned" that the other end of a rope tied to its foot is ALWAYS tied to a stake that it can't move. As an adult, it "remembers" that all ropes are tied to stakes it can't move. Consequently, even if the rope isn't tied down on the other end at all, the elephant won't try to walk away. The elephant is limited because it assumes it is limited. It accepts limitations based on the authority of its own assumptions.

Many of us are limited like this. We decide beforehand what our limits are without trying to reach further. In fact, some of us are so much smarter than elephants that we don't even have to have someone tie a rope around our legs before we limit ourselves.

---

[28] In the Interactive Teaching Method, we call this confusing linguistic behavior an Order of Magnitude Fault and we devote a great deal of time and attention training students to recognize and eliminate these faults from their writing and speech.

Just because we believe language is limited is no reason for us not to do our best to use language well. Language is a tool, not an answer. If we become so impressed by the limits we perceive about language to the point of becoming lazy, we may end up not experimenting with or challenging our limits as Alexander challenged himself and his limits. Without challenging our limits in language, we may never know the joys, the wealth, the riches we may share by overcoming our personal limitations, if only for just one phrase, one sentence, or one idea.

I do not believe that the teaching of this work can always be done through language alone, but I will guarantee that the amount of learning that can be done by "words alone" is much larger than most Alexander teachers usually think. For example, F.M.'s brother, A.R. Alexander, was the only other teacher for whom F.M. seemed to have consistent and high regard. Not only did A.R. claim that he needed just six lessons to learn the work, but he BOASTED that he never had to have hands placed on him.[29] In other words, the entire training of the only teacher in whom F.M. had enduring and consistent faith was accomplished through words alone! More importantly, prior to the innovations introduced in the middle and late thirties by the junior teachers on the early training courses, the emphasis in teaching and training the work was centered on verbal understanding.[30]

This is all a long preface to explain why I have included the phrase "in movement" in the One Thought.

Yes, I realize that I said that we are always in movement but by including the phrase "in movement" in the One Thought I wish to emphasize this point once more. More importantly, "in movement" is a kind of concession to our more common ideas about what the word "movement" usually means. Movement in this sense is also meant to convey being in activity where activity is construed to be purposeful movement, such as walking, talking, or scratching your nose.

---

[29] Both the story and the verb came from Marjory Barlow during a lecture at the 2nd International Congress of Alexander Teachers at Brighton, England.

[30] This contention is supported by Walter Carrington in his book, *Explaining the Alexander Technique* (with Seán Carey, Sheildrake Press, London, 1992, p. 9). In this book, Walter claims that, "In the early stages of his teaching he was still verbalizing the Technique to his pupils ... But certainly by the 1930's, he'd given up trying to explain the Technique in that way. I think it was his experience with the students on the first teacher training course that changed his perspective ... I think the experience of the first training course was shattering for him. It nearly sent him up the wall."

From this, one is left with the very clear impression that the switch in emphasis away from the use of language in teaching and more towards an emphasis on the use of hands was for the benefit of the early training course participants rather than a change in strategy decided upon independently by Alexander.

At the same time, there are also the internal movements of parts interacting with parts even when we are standing, sitting, or lying "still." So, "in movement" in this context means both of these kinds of actions, both the internalized and the purposeful movements.

*   *   *   *   *

ONE THOUGHT:

**the poise of a person's head
in relation with his or her body
in movement
is the key
to freedom**

I rarely have to explain to anyone what a "key" is. It's anything that can be used to allow access to something that has been previously withheld. In this case, the key is an idea, the first of many that we will be discussing. It is also a movement about which we will have more to say later.

Right now, however, I want to discuss the last point of this partial definition in greater detail.

For years, I used to say the last phrase in the One Thought – "freedom and ease of motion" – as though it was a single, complex noun: "freedomandeaseofmotion." Some of my colleagues still do. By saying these words in this way, what I gained in time was greatly outweighed by what I lost in meaning. By making this phrase into a single, complex noun, I was cheating myself and my students of a profound truth, i.e., that Mr. Alexander's work is the key to freedom. Period. Full stop.

Boundless freedom.

Unqualified freedom.

Freedom that means every bit of whatever "freedom" means to you.

By the time a person has learned to monitor and control this physiologic relationship to his advantage, he will have developed a mental discipline that will enable him to realize his dreams and to acquire all of the tools he will need to exceed all of his self-imposed limitations.

Sometimes, by focusing down on the details of particular results, I think we lose sight of the great scope and value of this work's potential. Therefore, in order to preserve a proper sense of scope, I choose not to make the phrase "freedom and ease of motion" into a single, complex noun, but rather I choose to talk about freedom in as large a sense as I can, because personal freedom in its largest sense is one of the great by-products of this work.

ONE THOUGHT:

the poise of a person's head
in relation with his or her body
in movement
is the key
to freedom
and ease of motion.

The other great by-product of this work that this beginning thought tells us about is "ease of motion". This is a phrase that has become a specialized, technical term among many of the students who worked with and trained with Marjorie Barstow in Nebraska. By "ease of motion," we mean the accomplishment of tasks and activities with a particular vital quality of movement in the performance of them. The nature of this particular quality includes, among other things, the elements of strength, efficiency, clarity of intent, and freedom from distortion.

I have found that, for most people, the concept of ease of motion can best be conveyed in a simple three-word phrase: "Fred Astaire dancing". For anyone who has seen him dance in films, it is easy to recognize in Mr. Astaire's dancing exactly the kinds of qualities that are meant by the phrase "ease of motion." His dancing also demonstrates another important point about coordination and control of movement. Control of movement has at least as much to do with the turning off of muscles, as it has to do with turning them on. To create his effects, Mr. Astaire always used just as much strength and effort as his actions required, and no more.

Now, I suspect that once I started talking about Fred Astaire dancing some of you started to think to yourselves, "Now he's gone too far! I can understand that this Alexander Technique stuff can help me. I might even move better, look better, feel better, and have more energy. But, I couldn't possibly learn to move as easily as Fred Astaire danced!"

HOW DO YOU KNOW?

Beware of your own elephant ropes!

*   *   *   *   *

At this point in my introductory classes, I usually begin working with students individually to show them more clearly what these words mean. By teaching these lessons in a group, it is usually quite easy to demonstrate the truth of this One Thought to the class's satisfaction. It also gives the teacher a chance to emphasize several aspects of the One Thought with which this work begins.

One of these aspects is the concept of "in relation with."

When I first begin working with each student (usually as the student sits), I ask everyone in the class if the student has everything he or she needs in order to do the Alexander Technique. In other words, does the student have a head and does the student have a body? I simply refuse to work with any student who does not have both. Having ascertained by close observation that the student has both, I am ready to begin teaching.

As the students are trying to figure out how to react to my silliness, I ask them more seriously if there is a relationship between the person's head and body. After they consider this for a while, they begin to understand that, because we are talking about two separate and different aspects of the same person, by necessity, there is a relationship between each person's head and body.

I then sometimes ask them if this relationship is static or in motion.

By now, whatever laughter there once was has stopped, because this question requires more involved thought than the students suspected was coming.

During the course of my writings, as during the course of my classes, students will be presented with hard choices and tough decisions. I do not expect or want anyone to accept every decision I have made. I do, however, want everyone to go through at least similar processes of evaluating and deciding things for themselves as I have. In other words, I don't care whether people agree with me or not. I only care that the quality of the process by which they reached their decisions and the amount of effort that they put into reaching them was at least as rigorous as my own.

I bring all of this up only because we have just reached an important point of decision.

When faced with the question as to whether this relationship of the head with the body is static or dynamic, most students opt for some kind of mixture. They report that their heads were in a fixed relationship to their bodies until they "changed positions." While they were moving their heads from "position" to "position," then, the relationship was dynamic. Once they got to the new "position," the relationship became fixed again.

Some people are very comfortable with this explanation.

I am not.

What if the reason why the movement of the head seems fixed at some times and not fixed at others is because the smallest unit of movement that we perceive is too big? What if we could become more and more sensitive, more refined in our ability to perceive smaller and smaller units of movement? If we did, then wouldn't the times when this relationship of our heads with our bodies was dynamic seem to increase, and the times this relationship was fixed seem to decrease?

This phenomenon is exactly what we observe in students who take lessons.

As their sensitivity to themselves in movement increases, the times they report their heads to be "not moving" dramatically decreases and the times they notice movement in this relationship increases. In fact, this trend is so universal and so endless as students become increasingly sensitive, that it has led me to postulate, as I have stated above, that we are constantly in motion, and that the relationships of all parts of us with respect to all our other parts are constantly in motion. As we shall see, some of these relationships may be more important than others, but they are all dynamic.

ONE THOUGHT:

**the poise of a person's head
in relation with his or her body
in movement
is the key
to freedom
and ease of motion.**

Chapter 5
TWO DISCOVERIES

DEPENDING ON how specific and detailed one chooses to be, the list of Alexander's discoveries could be very long indeed. If one decides to limit oneself to those discoveries that are basic to the work and which make the work unique, however, the list becomes much shorter. In fact, all that Alexander discovered can be distilled into a combination of two discoveries.

The first discovery that Alexander made was that in every movement you make there is a change in the relationship of your head with your body which precedes and accompanies the movement, and which will either be helpful to you or get in your way. In other words, every time you move, there is a change in the relationship of your head with your body that initiates or organizes the movement throughout your mechanism.

This movement will take on one of two major characteristics.

Either you will move your head in such a way as to increase the amount of muscular tension in your neck – a tension that will distort all succeeding relationships within you, pull you "out of shape", and lower the standard level of your general performance and coordination, OR, you will move your head in such a way that there will be a reduction in the amount of local and general muscular tension so that your system will subtly shift to conform to more natural and attractive internal relationships and your motor coordination in the performance of your activities will be enhanced. The enhancement of your coordination in the performance of activities will, in turn, improve the quality of the performance itself.

Because the Alexander Technique can train you to monitor and, ultimately, control this relationship of your head with your body (albeit indirectly), the nature of your coordination and the quality of your performance in activity will then become increasingly a matter of choice. Through the Alexander Technique, constant improvement in both coordination and performance quality is readily attainable.

*   *   *   *   *

In other words, every movement can be thought of as being made up of two kinds of movements.

The first of these is the kind of movement we were talking about before when we talked about the movements of relationships between body parts. In the Interactive Teaching Method, we call these primary movements the "organizing"[31] movements and to understand them better, let's first take a look at a basic concept from anatomy.

Anatomists distinguish between the two different kinds of "skeleton" that make up the "rigid" framework of our bodies. That is, they divide the skeleton into two different groupings: the axial skeleton and the appendicular skeleton. The axial skeleton is made up of the skull, the spine, the ribs, the sternum, and, according to some authors, the hyoid.[32] The axial skeleton constitutes the "rigid" central framework of the head and body. The remaining bones – shoulder blade, collar bone, humerus, etc. of the upper limb and the innominate, femur, etc. in the lower limb – make up the appendicular skeleton.

The organizing movements take place primarily in the axial structures. They either improve the capacity to perform a task by creating a flexible condition in the axial structures moving within small and balanced ranges of motion OR they decrease the capacity to perform a task by changing the relationships of the axial structures in such a way as to compress or overstretch them outside this optimal range of motion in a way that leads to or promotes a condition of either "collapse" or other fixtures and rigidity. The resulting condition of the axial structures will, in turn, influence the relative efficiency of the organizing movements in the appendicular structures as well.

The second aspect of every movement is that combination of changes in joint angulations that are peculiar to, and characteristic of, the action being performed. In this regard, we might call these combinations of motions the task-specific movements – the changes in joint angulations that define the movement itself.

---

[31] In the first two editions of this book, I called these movements "relationing" movements. This choice was originally made to conform with current word usage in Nebraska through the eighties. Since then I have found the phrase "organizing movements" to be a much more effective term, one more easily understood by students. Similarly, I have chosen in this edition to replace the word "gestural" with the hypenated phrase "task-specific". Again I hope this will prove to be a beneficial change.

[32] This is a curious inclusion because the hyoid is not actually a bone and is made up entirely of cartilage. The reason for its inclusion is most likely the fact that, even though it is not a bone, the hyoid acts like a bone in that it is a very important attachment point for many muscles in the front of the neck. Therefore, to the authors who include the hyoid in the axial skeleton, because the hyoid "acts" like a bone, it "counts" as a bone.

This is an excellent example of the concept that "facts" in even as straightforward a science as gross anatomy are as much a function of assumptions, definitions, and opinions as they are a function of "reality".

Task-specific movements may be restricted to one joint, or may be expanded to include all of them. Task-specific movements may involve either the axial or appendicular skeletons, or both. They may involve brief, momentary protocols, or may take place over a very long period of time. Whatever the nature of the task-specific movements, they are always preceded and accompanied by organizing movements which either help the quality of the performance of the task-specific movements or which get in the way. As you will see, the choice – help or hurt – is up to you.

The first of Alexander's two combined discoveries, therefore, could be summarized in this way:

1. In every movement you make, there is a change in the relationship of your head with your body that precedes and accompanies the movement, and which either helps you or gets in your way.

In other words, every movement is made up of two kinds of movements:

   i. Organizing movements performed primarily by axial structures that determine the quality of the task-specific movements, and

   ii. Task-specific movements that are the combination of joint angulation changes that make up any specific action and which can involve any part of the body.

*   *   *   *   *

The second thing that Alexander discovered is, if anything, more important than the first discovery. As a result of his reasoning and experimentation, Alexander discovered that the conscious mind has the capacity to override every system, including the natural ones. In other words, Alexander discovered that our conscious minds have the power to give us control of our own potentialities or to prevent us forever from becoming all that we can be.

Many people believe that there are certain aspects of our system and our functioning that are beyond our capacity for interference. They believe that there are some things that we just can't mess up with our meddlesome minds and ideas. As it turns out, this concept is wrong. In fact, it is our ability to impose our concepts and ideas upon our movement behavior that is responsible for the bizarre and bewildering variation in performance and appearance that is evident in any large group of people.

For instance, many of my students have the idea that it is necessary to tighten the anterior thigh muscles to remain standing. It is not. The "natural systems" of the body work in such a way that, once a person has made the decision to stand and is standing, no great muscular effort is required in the legs to maintain this posture, and, if, as some authors claim, muscular effort is required, the muscles they claim are required to function in such a case are located in the calves. In the standing posture, therefore, the anterior thigh muscles (the quadriceps femoris) should be largely uninvolved. If we were to find someone whose anterior thigh muscles were tight while standing (and it is easy to do), we would have to search for another reason other than the necessity of mechanics for this tightness.

In my experience, the major reason why people have tight anterior thigh muscles while standing is because they mistakenly believe they have to use these muscles to stand. Many of the people who think they need to use these muscles in standing have heavily overdeveloped thigh muscles. They also want to blame their unwanted "size" on fat. In most cases, this extra "size" is actually the result of a kind of continuous isometric contraction of these muscles, and the only reason for this enforced contraction is the student's mistaken concept about the need to keep these muscles tight.[33]

Similarly, many people do not realize that there are two functional joints in the elbow region. Everyone is familiar with the hinge-like joint in the middle of the arm that allows us to bend our forearms toward our upper arms or to straighten our arms out. Not everyone realizes that there is another joint in the elbow region about an inch closer to the hand.

This joint is called the proximal radio-ulnar joint, and its purpose is to allow us to roll the moveable radius bone over the top of the relatively fixed ulnar bone. This joint allows us to turn our palms up relative to our arms, as when we are receiving change at a cash register, or to turn our palms downward, as when we type or play the piano, without having to move the upper arm.

I wish I had a nickel for every pianist who claimed to be an expert about the arm and its requirements for efficient movement who didn't even know that this joint existed!!! I think I could comfortably retire on the interest from the principal that such a piano tax would generate.

The fancy name for this alternating movement is pronation and supination of the forearm. It is normal for this joint to move 180 degrees – or one complete half turn – from palm up to palm down without moving the upper arm. I cannot remember meeting any adult who still had full range of motion in this joint without having some form of previous help, either clinical or educational. One of the major reasons why I think this is true is that most people don't even know that this movement is possible. Over time, this conceptual fault has resulted in an artificial restriction of movement behavior.

---

[33] For a more complete discussion on muscle function and physiology, see chapters 7 and 8.

Sometimes, even after we have been told what is possible, we are so certain that our erroneous movement beliefs are correct that we will often deny our own experience. My favorite example of this happened one time when I was working with a pianist on a piano technique called a tremolo.

A tremolo is accomplished by rapidly alternating between pushing down one key with the thumb and then another key (usually an octave away) with the little finger. I was struck by the ingenuity of this particular pianist because she was performing this movement without using the radio-ulnar joints at all. By a combination of finger, wrist, shoulder, and body movements she was able to alternate the notes quickly, but she understandably complained about fatigue.

When I showed her how to accomplish the same thing using this "new" joint, she argued with me that what I was showing her wasn't possible – even as she did it! Then, after she had been doing this rapid alternation using her forearm in this way for some time, she stopped and turned to me and said, "I can't do this!"

"You can't do what?" I asked innocently.

She then brought her arm up, turned it back and forth perfectly, just as I had shown her, and said, "I can't do this."

"You can't do what?" I repeated inoffensively.

"This!" she shouted wildly, as she continued the movement.

"What?" I asked again, somewhat fiendishly.

This time as she continued to perform the movement and was about to say, "This!" once more, it gradually dawned upon her that in order to show me the movement she claimed she couldn't do, she had to perform the movement itself. In fact, she performed it very well. Still, her conviction that she couldn't do that movement completely overrode her own understanding that she was doing the very thing she claimed that she couldn't do, even as she did it.

Once she understood the contradiction, we both laughed.

Her conviction about her inability to perform this movement was so strong, however, that the very next thing that she said after we had stopped laughing was, "Well, I still can't do it"

Furthermore, these kinds of self-imposed and self-created limitations do not require ignorance in order to happen.

Once I had a registered nurse (who was also an Alexander teacher) in one of my anatomy classes when I was talking about the elbow region. When I claimed that there was a second joint in the elbow region that accomplished pronation and supination, she loudly exclaimed, "No!" Intrigued by her response, I asked her to show me how to pronate and supinate without using that second joint. She then twisted and turned her humerus (her upper arm bone) in her shoulder joint while holding her elbow region in place.

Now this was a person who had studied anatomy, passed exams, and taken a cadaver dissection class. She had even taught anatomy to other nurses. She "knew" all of the information about the region, but her own personal idea of the way the region worked was different from what she had studied. She believed her personal ideas more than the information she had learned. In fact, she believed her personal ideas more than the information she had taught. Therefore, the way she turned her forearm conformed to her personal ideas rather than to what she had learned and taught about the body structures themselves.

When I told her that the arm was constructed to move differently than the way she had demonstrated and that it moved more efficiently in this other way, she didn't believe me. In fact, in spite of her recall command of the anatomy in that region, she completely denied that her arm could move in the way that I described. When I offered to show her how her arm really worked, she almost dared me to try. When I actually moved her arm as it was made to be moved, the experience was in such conflict with her ideas that her eyes flew open in surprise and she cried out, "You broke it!"

*　　　　*　　　　*　　　　*　　　　*

Our conscious minds have the capacity to override every system – our sensory system, our manner of movement, even our reflexes.[34]

Alexander discovered that what we think and how we think it can have a tremendous effect on the functioning of our mechanism. Like the organizing movement of our head with our body, the effect of our manner of thinking can be

---

[34] In orthopedic testing, Jandrassik's Maneuver is used to eliminate conscious interference by the patient in testing for deep tendon reflexes of the knee. The test is used in those cases when the clinician is unable to elicit a normal reflex response after striking the patient on the infrapatellar tendon with a reflex hammer. Sometimes, however, a normal response will be absent in people who do not have any neurologic problems.

To determine if the diminished response is pathologic or not, the patient is asked to lock his fingers together and pull outward on his hands as if to pull them apart while the clinician strikes the infrapatellar tendon once more. In cases where there is no pathology, the patient will usually be so busy pulling on his hands, he will forget to interfere with the patellar reflex and a normal response can be elicited. This normal response is possible because the patient is no longer preventing it by a bleed-over, conscious interference generated by the patient's ideas.

for our benefit or our detriment. And it doesn't matter if you believe in these principles or not, they are in operation in everything you do.

No matter what you believe, you are going to precede and accompany every task-specific movement (activity) you perform with organizing movements of your axial and appendicular structures in such a way that you are either helped or hindered. You are going to "create and operate" yourself based upon your ideas of what is right and wrong, and your "natural system" will adapt itself to fit your ideas in a kind of self-fulfilling prophesy, even to the point of distortion and structural damage in activity.

Or, as Flip Wilson's comedic character Geraldine might say, "What you think is what you get!"[35]

Now you can believe all this or not. You can ignore this information or not. It doesn't matter. What I am sharing with you is true, and there are many other places where you can find this same information.

What makes it uniquely Alexander's is that he says that the combined manifestation of these truths occurs even at the levels of planning, structure, and movement behavior. What you think and how you think it determines, to a great extent, what you will be and become.

This being so, then doesn't it make sense to learn about the operative and formative principles which Alexander articulated? Doesn't it make sense to learn these principles and use them to acquire a universally constant improvement in your standard level of general performance? Doesn't it make sense to learn and use these principles so that you can free yourself from your own self-imposed limitations in every movement and endeavor?

Of course it does. And that's why I'm here to help you.

---

[35]   Flip Wilson was an American character comedian whose popularity was just beginning to wane as the first edition of this book came out, but many of his character's taglines had entered into common usage in the States.

Geraldine was one of his most popular characters and was created by Wilson putting on a really bad wig and wearing some of the worst designed, cheapest, trashiest outfits ever made. The effect was to make "Geraldine" appear like a low class streetwalker who was in more danger of arrest from the fashion police than the vice squad.

What endeared this character to us was her indomitable self-esteem and attitude. Although she had to be one of the worst looking creatures ever to wear a dress, she continued to see herself as desirable, continued to flirt with men for the sole purpose of taking them home, and, whenever confronted with doubts or aspersions about her character or appearance, she deflected these critical comments and looks from her potential love-victims by defiantly reminding them that "What you see is what you get!"

ALEXANDER'S TWO DISCOVERIES:

1. In every movement you make, there is a change in the relationship of your head with your body that precedes and accompanies the movement and which either helps you or gets in your way.

   In other words, in every movement there are two kinds of movements:

   i. Organizing movements performed primarily by the axial structures which EITHER create a flexible condition that improves the coordination of the movement OR which create an overstretched fixture or a general "collapse" that lowers the coordination of the movement, and

   ii. Task-specific movements which are made up of changes in the angles of the joints in the functional regions of the body and which define the actual movement itself.

2. The conscious mind has the capacity to override every system, including the natural ones.

   In other words, the conscious mind has the power to give us control of our own potentialities OR to prevent us forever from becoming all that we can be.

WHAT YOU THINK IS WHAT YOU GET

Chapter 6
THE MONKEY TRAP

IN HIS BOOK, *Freedom to Change,* Frank Pierce Jones tells us that "a simple way to trap a monkey is to present him with a nut in a bottle. The monkey puts his paw through the bottle's narrow mouth, grasps the nut, then cannot withdraw his paw because he will not (and hence cannot) let go of the nut."[36]

In the eighties, I would often include this story in an introductory class because people could understand it easily and quickly. They could understand how a monkey might see a nut in a bottle, grab it, and not let go. Because the monkey could just barely squeeze his empty paw into the bottle, and because holding the nut in his paw makes his paw larger, the monkey traps himself.

In terms of Alexander and his work, the nature of this transaction is very simple.

When the monkey sees the nut, it acts as a stimulus and the monkey decides to get the nut. In this way, the nut becomes the "end" the monkey wishes to "gain." By acting immediately upon the desire to get the nut directly, the monkey falls victim to something we call "end-gaining" in the Alexander Technique. His attention is on the end he wishes to gain (the nut), so he pays little or no attention to the circumstances present or the manner in which he will gain his end. In fact, he just reaches for the nut and grabs it.

In and of itself, the act of reaching directly for a nut is not a problem. If the nut had been out in the open, it would have been a suitable strategy. In such a case, it may easily have been the most efficient strategy possible. But, this particular nut is not out in the open. It is in a particular kind of bottle with particular characteristics. As a result, the movement strategy which had once served the monkey extremely well, and which had helped him to survive before, now endangers him. If the monkey persists in his old strategy, it will prove deadly.

There is nothing wrong with the strategy. The strategy and its effectiveness haven't changed. What have changed are the circumstances that surround the use of the strategy. What was once of great value is now a danger because the conditions in which this strategy will be employed are different. If the monkey persists in his usual manner of response, if he continues to put his attention on the end he wishes to gain, if he seeks to gain his end directly without consideration of how

---

[36] Jones, Frank Pierce, *Freedom to Change.* Mouritz, London, 1997, p. 4.

he gets it, and if he doesn't put his attention on learning how to change the manner of his response to this new, nutty stimulus, he will be caught.

Usually at this point in my presentation, I would ask my students to take a few minutes and tell me some other solutions to the monkey's dilemma. I'd like you to do this, too.

Take a few minutes and write down as many different solutions as you can think of to this problem of getting a nut without getting caught. I'll wait for you. When you are finished, read on.

$$* \qquad * \qquad * \qquad * \qquad *$$

I am always surprised by how enthusiastic and creative people can be while doing this assignment. Their responses almost always turn into one of the most fun experiences in these introductory classes. I have been doing this demonstration for over twenty years now and I am still getting new solutions.

How many solutions did you have? I'd like to share with you now the three most common categories of solutions that I have received.[37]

The first category of solutions is the largest and it often contains the most creative ideas. Most students try first to think of a different way to get the nut out of the bottle.

Some of the ways that have been suggested are: 1) shake the nut out, 2) break the bottle[38], 3) for Looney Tune fans, there is the world-famous chewing gum on the end of a stick strategy, 4) a hydraulic engineer once suggested washing the nut out on a wave of water, and 5) in the late eighties, I taught three consecutive classes in which the students suggested sucking the nut out.[39]

The second category of answer involves performing some sort of operation on the nut while it is in the bottle so that the nut opens. Then, the smaller, edible pieces of the nut can be easily and safely extracted.

---

[37] If you've thought of a solution that doesn't seem to fit any of these categories, please send me a postcard and tell me about it. I love to find new solutions.

[38] For aficionados, this sub-category runs the range from getting a hippo to break the bottle for you, which has the dual attraction of not cutting yourself on the broken glass and opening the nut as well (although no good solution has yet been found to the problem of ingesting broken glass), all the way to the monkey using the diamond on her new engagement ring to cut out the bottom of the bottle and then reach for the nut through that larger opening. (Could you tell that this last student had just received an engagement ring herself?)

[39] I have no idea what this means.

The last solution is the one that people rarely think of. I am always very proud of the people who do think of it. It involves a form of solution that requires a "trick of mind" that many people find hard to accomplish. In order to understand this mind trick better, let's see if we can find the solution to a simple problem which was once posed to me in a math class.

Picture if you will nine dots arranged in this fashion:

•   •   •

•   •   •

•   •   •

Your task is to connect all nine dots by using only four straight lines and without raising your pencil from the paper once you have started drawing lines.

Go ahead and try to work this out. The answer, if you need it, can be found in Appendix B.

*   *   *   *   *

As we have seen in Appendix B, the solution is found in being able to go outside the self-imposed limits of the problem as you perceive it. No one told you to stay inside the "box" that the nine dots seem to make. In fact, there is no "box" to stay inside of. If you had trouble solving this puzzle, it was probably because you perceived these dots as a "box" and made another rule in your own mind about having to stay within these "perceived" – but unreal – boundaries.

In a similar way, people make up their own "perceived rules" about turning over on my portable adjusting table when I am giving them a chiropractic adjustment. Because the portable table is so much smaller and so much less stable than the tables I use in my office, many people complain about the "danger" as they go from lying on their back to lying on their stomach and vice versa. Almost everyone is uncomfortable as they do it.

There is one special group of people who are not uncomfortable when they "change sides." These are the people who, when I ask them to turn over, stand up first, and then turn appropriately as they get back on the table. They have no trouble turning at all. Rather than staying on the table and twisting precariously because they perceive that there are rules that say that they have to stay on the table, these people just step outside of the "box" and take care of their own needs.

The more I teach and the more I work as a physician, the more strongly I am struck by the number of problems that people cause for themselves because of self-imposed limitations from perceived but unreal rules. Some of my patients believe that they have to perform certain exercises or move in a certain way because of their injuries. In many cases, these peculiar ways of moving only serve to aggravate their condition. Further, very few of these patients are easily able to see their own participation in the exacerbation of their conditions.

This kind of behavior is really no different than the elephants that are tied up to "perceived" stakes in the ground. Except, perhaps, that it is more insidious. At least with the elephants, their handlers are using a real rope to trick them intentionally. In the cases of my students and patients, all too often the restrictive "9 dot boxes" or "elephant ropes" that hold my students back are being created by the captives themselves.

How does this relate to our friend the monkey?

Well, the third solution to satisfying his desire to get a nut is for him to forget about the nut in the bottle and go get another nut. Just because he sees the nut in the bottle and it makes him want to have a nut, it doesn't mean that he has to have that particular nut. There are a lot of nuts around, and, if the monkey doesn't believe that, he should come to some of my classes.

*   *   *   *   *

Once we believe that we have found all or most of the solutions to the monkey's problem, I ask my students what they did differently than the monkey in finding their solutions. Eventually, they tell me that there were two differences.

First of all, they point out that all of their solutions were more indirect then the one the monkey used. Rather than going immediately for their end in a direct manner, they stopped, looked at the situation, and made decisions about what was involved in the problem. Then, they addressed themselves to reasoning out a solution appropriate to the specific problem at hand. The use of this kind of reasoning behavior constitutes the second major difference between the approaches of the monkey and my students.

In Alexander terms, instead of keeping their attention on the end they wished to gain, my students put their attention on the means, the process, the way they could safely gain their end. At the heart of Alexander's work is this invitation to forego trying to gain your end directly and instead keeping your attention on reasoning out the *means* whereby you will gain your end instead.

Whenever my students are anxious about whether or not they will ever gain their ends, I remind them that if they simply perform the process they have reasoned out to gain their end, and if the process they have reasoned out is appropriate and the end is attainable, they cannot help but reach their end. In fact, they can't avoid it.

It is inevitable.

*   *   *   *   *

In the same paragraph in which Frank tells the story about the monkey trap, he goes on to say, "Most people are caught in monkey traps of unconscious habits."[40] If we are ever to get out of the self-imposed monkey traps of our unconscious habits, we will need a powerful tool. We will need a new way to look at ourselves, our movements, our feeling sense, our thoughts, and our concepts. We will need to learn how to look at these things in such a way that we will no longer be bound by them. We will need to learn to look at them so that they will come to serve us rather than bind us to our concepts of the tyranny of habit.

In order to put this new tool into use, we will need courage, discipline, and a willingness to work and experiment.

Alexander has supplied us with the tool.

The rest is up to us.

---

[40]   Jones, Frank Pierce, *Freedom to Change.* Mouritz, London, p. 4.

PHYSIOLOGIC CONSIDERATIONS

Chapter 7

HOW MUSCLES WORK

THE BEST WAY to understand the mechanics of what is actually going on as we move is to look at some basic concepts about the way in which our systems are put together and how they function. In this way, we can also get a clearer picture of what is going on in an Alexander lesson. Once we have a sense of how our mechanisms work, this will give us a foundation upon which to retrain our thinking processes so that we can make Alexander's work our own.

First of all, let's take a look at how muscles work.

Each muscle is made up of many fibers that are grouped together and attached into bundles. These bundles are grouped together into larger bundles, and then still larger bundles, until the largest grouping of these similarly located and oriented bundles of fibers is given a single name to designate a single muscle. In fact, there is a way in which giving a single muscle name to these groups of fibers is a kind of false distinction, in that it is possible for various small parts of any given muscle to fire at any given time while the rest of the muscle is at rest.

Muscles come in many shapes and sizes, and perform many different kinds of activities. It is the nature of the activity that needs to be performed which evolutionarily has determined the size and shape of the muscles. The muscles that we are most interested in right now are the ones that enable large movements at the joints.

*   *   *   *   *

Most typically, this kind of muscle is attached by a tendon to the bones on both sides of a joint.[41] The working part of the muscle, called the belly, lies between the two attachments. When the muscle is working – when it is turned "on" – the belly of the muscle contracts. As this happens, it pulls on the attachments at both ends of the muscle, bringing the two ends closer together. This

---

[41] When we think about our skeletons, we usually think of the bones that make them up. In order to understand movement, however, we have to think of our skeleton as being made up of bones and joints. A joint is the space between two or more bones in the skeleton. If there were no joints, our skeleton would be in a single piece like the shell of a crab, and we would be unable to move. So, the combination of bones and joints that make up our skeleton is what allows for the balance between the strength of the rigid framework that the bones provide, and the ability to move provided by the "spaces" of the joints. As we shall see, it is the function of our muscles to provide the power to move us at our joints.

contraction of the muscle is what provides the power to move the bones. In other words, it is the muscles of our body that provide the major source of power for movement, alignment, and distortion.

Many people are quite enamored of the concept that gravity is the great villain in the melodrama of our poor posture and movement. "Gravity is king!" one of my instructors from chiropractic school used to love to say, "All must bow down before gravity!"

I no longer think this is true. It seems to me that gravity does some wonderful things for us. As Marjorie Barstow used to say, it does keep us from floating off into space. But, within the closed system of our bodies, the effect of gravity with respect to making changes in the relationships of body parts to body parts is very small while the effect of our muscles, directed by our thoughts, is very large. Perhaps the most important point regarding gravity is not so much its potential relative influence upon us, as the probability that, over time, we have developed sufficiently as a species to function in harmony with our environment in spite of the force of gravity.

Referring to his own experience in lessons in his Noble Prize speech, Niko Tinbergen said:

> It is highly unlikely that in their very long evolutionary history of walking upright, the hominids have not had time to evolve the correct mechanisms for bipedal locomotion. This conclusion receives support from the surprising, but indubitable fact that even after 40 to 50 years of obvious misuse one's body can (one might say) snap back into proper, and in many respects more healthy, use as a result of a short series of half-hourly sessions. Proper stance and movement are obviously genetically old, environment-resistant behaviors.[42]

If Tinbergen is right, our bodies are normally very strong and can resist gravity in widely varying ways. It is only in cases of severe disability or disorder that people do not have the ability to function effectively within the constant gravitational field we all experience. While it would be nice to have something like gravity to blame for the distortions we experience and observe, it is clear that a single, relatively weak, unidirectional force such as gravity cannot account for the diversity of variations that we see. It does take a powerful force to cause the differences we see, but gravity is not the culprit. The force that fuels these distortions in each of us is the power and force of our muscles, directed by the power and force of our conscious minds.

---

[42]   Lindsten, Jan, ed., *Nobel Lectures in Physiology or Medicine 1971-1980.* World Scientific Publishing Co., Singapore, 1992.
(Also available at: http://www.nobel.se/medicine/laureates/1973/tinbergen-lecture.html)

In other words, the way in which we move and look depends mostly upon which muscles are contracted and which are not, the order in which they are contracted, and the amount of force with which they are contracted. Simply put: in any movement, some muscles are used primarily for movement, some for creating a stable support against which the movement muscles can pull, and some are used for fine correction of the movement once it has been initiated. And the starting point for all of this division of labor is found in what we are thinking.

As you have probably already guessed, this process can become quite involved. While it is essential for your teacher to know and understand these processes, you need only concern yourself with just a few basic ideas. In fact, there are only five most important things to remember about muscles and how they work.

*   *   *   *   *

The first most important thing to remember about muscles is that when they work, muscles get shorter. There are a number of elegant explanations about how this is done, and not a little bit of controversy, but the one thing that all of these different movement models agree upon is that when muscles work, they get shorter.

The second most important thing to know about muscles is that when they are not working, they do not get longer. They get less short.

This may seem like a picky distinction or a word game, but it is actually much more important than that. Although there is a mechanism for muscles to make themselves shorter, there is no mechanism for them to make themselves longer.[43]

As teachers and proponents of Alexander's ideas, we often talk about muscles or body parts "lengthening." Too often, in a practical sense, this encourages students to "do" something to lengthen. Students should not be encouraged to try to "lengthen" their muscles, because, philosophic discussions aside, it is not possible.

---

[43] Other Alexander teachers seem to disagree with this idea, most notably Wilfred Barlow. As I understand his argument, he says that lengthening is not accomplished by simply stopping contraction and implies that the muscle spindle is somehow responsible for actually mechanically lengthening the muscle. (Barlow, Wilfred, *The Alexander Principle*, The Guernsey Press Co., Ltd., C.I., 1998, pp. 73-76.) I, on the other hand, believe that simply stopping muscular contraction will indeed allow the muscle to return to its normal resting length (as a function of physical properties within the muscles), and while there is no question that the muscle spindles play an important role in the monitoring of muscle length, their actual function is proprioceptive and regulatory, not mechanical.

The act of "lengthening" which generates the corresponding feeling-sense impression comes primarily from the result of stopping prior on-going contractions in the muscle. Because it takes energy to contract a muscle, once this effort of contraction stops – that is, in the absence of the energy required to make the muscle shorter – the muscle quietly returns to its natural resting length. This allows the muscles to become less short, not to lengthen. In other words, muscles do not actively get longer. When they are not working, muscles get less short.

For example, it is not unusual for a student in an Alexander lesson to appear taller during a lesson. My own personal record for the greatest amount of change of height in a student during a single lesson was measured at six and a half inches (16.5 centimeters), where the standing height of the individual at the end of his lesson was six and a half inches higher than it was listed on his driver's license.

Now, in understanding what happened, it is important to see that the student did not really get taller. He got less short. As I am sure some of you have already guessed (or seen elsewhere in a class), the student's previous lower height was primarily the result of compressions and the exaggeration of the normal spinal curves caused by excessive muscular pulls, creating in him a very exaggerated slump. In other words, his decreased stature was caused by the constant shortening of a number of muscles. As I worked with him, the distorting pulls of the various muscles generally became less. In other words, the muscles involved in creating his distortion worked less; as a result, the muscles involved in creating the distortion got less short; the distortion, in turn, diminished; and the student's height increased.

The third most important thing to remember about how muscles work is that they can be thought of as being grouped in opposing pairs of flexor and extensor muscles. For just about every muscle or group of muscles in the body that pull a bone in one direction, there is another muscle or group of muscles that pull the bone in the opposite direction.

For instance, the best-known muscle in the upper arm is the Biceps muscle. The action of this muscle, located anatomically on the front of the arm, is to bend the forearm towards the upper arm at the hinge joint in the elbow.[44] Located on the back of the arm is another muscle called the Triceps whose job is to straighten the bend caused at the elbow joint by the Biceps muscle.

---

[44] It is worth mentioning that it is the contraction of the muscle fibers in the biceps in the process of moving the forearm that causes the muscle to bulge and become hard. It is not, as some people believe, moving the arm by some mysterious means that causes the muscle to bulge. While this may be obvious to some, it may not be to others. It is the shortening of muscle fibers that causes movement thereby making a change in the muscle's shape. It is not "movement" that causes "muscles" to show more clearly.

While this structure of opposing pairs of muscles is not always this clear in the rest of the body, the principle of muscles working in opposing "pairs" almost always applies. For just about every muscle that moves a bone one way, there is another muscle that moves it back.

The fourth most important thing to remember about how muscles work is that muscles only have a direct effect on the joint the muscle crosses. The direct effect of a muscle ends at the muscle's attachments.

On the face of it, the idea that the direct effect of a muscle occurs only in the joint or joints that the muscle spans, and goes no further than the attachments of the muscles, may seem obvious. My experience with students shows me, however, that in terms of practical application, the majority of people do not understand this principle at all.

Let's take as an example someone with a tremendous slump that is having a lesson.

One of the major causes for this kind of slump is that, as part of the general pattern of his misuse, the muscles at the back of the neck as well as the muscles in the front of the body are working too much and have pushed or pulled the head and other parts in various ways so that the upper part of the body moves unduly forward and curves over upon itself. As we have talked about above and seen repeatedly in classes, if these muscles would stop overly contracting, the interference would diminish, the distortion would lessen, and the slump would decrease. While we might all agree about these mechanics for this distortion, some people use at least one strategy for getting rid of this kind of slump on which we might not agree.

Have you ever tightened the muscles in your legs in an attempt to lengthen your torso? It's really quite a common response. And really quite ineffectual. Actually detrimental. Most people, once they understand how muscles work, can agree that turning on a leg muscle isn't a good strategy to effect a change in the torso. In fact, because of the increase in muscular tension in the legs, this strategy probably causes more problems than it solves. But why doesn't it work?

Two reasons.

In the first place, the muscles most commonly tightened are attached to, or end at, the pelvis or even lower on the femur. The joints these muscles span are not located in the trunk. Consequently, their actions cannot directly affect the area of distortion that lies beyond (superior to) these attachments.

More to the point, the student's problem is being caused by too much contraction in the first place. Further contraction of even more muscles in the leg will not prevent the interference and distortion created by too much muscular contraction in the neck and torso. Only diminishing the amount of undue contraction in the neck and torso muscles that are creating the slump will provide a real solution.

Even if one were to contract the muscles whose action opposes the "slumping" muscles – an idea we will talk about later – all one would succeed in doing would be to have two sets of unnecessarily contracted muscles instead of just one set. You might be "straighter," but you would be stiffer as well and you would still be carrying out the act and motion of slumping. The only difference would be that now you would be "slumping" and "straightening" at the same time!

Not a great solution if efficiency and ease of motion is your goal.

And this is the fifth most important thing to remember about muscles in relation to this work.

Motion at a joint is caused primarily by the sum effect of all of the muscular forces being brought to bear on the bones that make up that joint. Since the greatest efficiency in movement would involve the greatest amount of work done for the least amount of effort, we can easily state the minimum amount of effort needed to perform any activity in a formula. I call this formula the Motion Needs Equation:

1. For every movement, some muscles will have to be fired (contracted) to power the movement; some muscles will have to be fired to create the stability required to perform the movement; and some muscles will have to be fired to provide mid-course corrections for fine-tuning the movement.

2. For each of these actions, there is a minimum amount of effort required to meet the needs of the motion and task involved.

3. Any effort greater than this is unnecessary and wasteful. Therefore, these three kinds of actions should be performed with the least amount of effort required.

4. Much more importantly, all of the other muscles – the ones not involved in these three kinds of actions – serve purposes that are not required for the performance of the given motion and hence should be turned off.

If we return to our friend who is tightening his legs to prevent his slump, we see a number of ways in which this activity is contrary to the motion needs equation.

In the first place, because of the location of the leg muscles – because their end attachments are lower on the body than the areas involved in the slump – these muscles cannot be considered to be used for the purpose of making the motion involved or for fine-tuning the motion once begun. More importantly, the addition of even greater amounts of effort to remedy a problem caused by too much effort already is a strategy that makes no sense.

I suppose that someone might argue or believe that the leg muscles could be used to stabilize the body in order to perform the action of "straightening up" to eliminate the slump. Certainly if one were to try to eliminate the slump by activating the muscles which straighten the body and thereby increase the amount of forces involved, there might be a need to stiffen the legs to "stabilize" these additional unnecessary muscular forces. But, this kind of slump (and most other body distortions) is being caused by too much muscular effort in the first place. A more reasonable approach would be to eliminate the original fault by turning off the muscles causing the problem.

*   *   *   *   *

By putting these ideas together, we can begin to see the body and its condition in a new and exciting way.

Motion is caused by the contraction of muscles. When the force of muscular contraction acting on a bone in one direction is greater than the force of muscular contractions acting on that bone in any other direction, this will cause the bone to turn around another bone at the joint in a manner which allows the ends of the contracting muscle to come closer together. If the contracting force of an opposing muscle, pulling at the same time and in a direction opposite to the pull of the first muscle, was of the same amount of force as the first, the forces would cancel each other out, the bone would not turn around the joint, and there would be no "motion".

But, there would be "movement". In fact, there would be two "movements": one pulling in one direction and the other pulling in the opposite direction.

This kind of kinetic stalemate is what we mean when we say that someone is "holding a position." It is not that these people are being "still" so much as they are involved in a kind of balancing tug of war in which they are trying to move in at least two opposing directions at once. The resulting muscular overaction serves no useful purpose but rather layers on successive amounts of purposeless force. This purposeless muscular force is what we usually mean by tension.

As an Alexander teacher and a doctor, I often hear clients complain that they "carry their tension" in their shoulders or neck or legs or wherever. They believe, incorrectly, that tension is some kind of entity, some kind of condition with a life of its own that can be carried around like coins in a pocket. When I work with these people and they experience relief from the tension they have caused themselves in one area, quite often they tell me that their "tension" has moved to another area (where they are continuing to cause "tension" in themselves). I understand what they are saying to me and why they say it, but I think they are wrong. I will tell you why.

There is no such thing as tension!

No such THING. Things exist by themselves, on their own. They don't require someone to be constantly making them. They don't require a constant input of energy and direction from an outside source. And this is why your "tension" is not a "THING" because, without you putting in the energy to make it happen, it doesn't exist.

In other words, your "tension" isn't carried around. Your "tension" isn't transferred. Your "tension" doesn't even exist. "Tension" is nothing more nor less than a persistent and unnecessary combination of "movements" of constant and purposeless muscular contraction that people habitually carry out to their detriment, often as part of a more complex pattern of habitual movements. The impression that your tension has "moved" most often comes from the experience of stopping unnecessary muscular tension in one region only to become aware of continuing, unnecessary muscular tension in another region that was there already but overshadowed by the feeling of tension in the muscles now released.

Tension is simply a combination of "movements" that you carry out continuously against yourself. There is no such THING as tension because if you didn't make it, it wouldn't exist. If you have "tension", it is because you have made it and continue to make it at all times. But that's good. Because if you caused it, you can stop it. You don't have to wait for anyone or anything else.

*   *   *   *   *

These are the major elements of muscle physiology that have a bearing on the Alexander Technique. By putting all of this information together, we can see that the power of our muscles is the most important physical element in the creation of our distortions.

When our muscles are working in a balanced way that satisfies the motion needs equation for a given movement, this use of our muscles provides harmony and an increased quality of performance. When the use of our muscles is out of balance and in violation of the motion needs equation, the muscles produce distortions and a decrease in the quality of performance.

How our muscles come to be in these maladaptive conditions and, more importantly, how we can learn to retrain ourselves to perform in more constructive ways lies at the heart of the Alexander Technique. But in order to move ahead in learning about these procedures, we must first look more closely at the relationship between movement and thought.

Chapter 8

THE IMMACULATE CONTRACTION

WHILE MUSCLES provide the power for movement, it is our nervous system that provides the direction of our movements. Muscles are only machines that contract on command. The message to contract comes from the nerves. Some of the messages that reach the muscles, such as reflexes, are built into the system and cannot be easily changed directly. Other messages are elaborate, on-going strategies for turning certain muscle groups on and off in specific sequences. These sequences constitute the design of a given movement.

It is impossible to change the design of a movement once the message has been sent out of the motor area of the brain. It is only before that point – as the movement is being designed – that a change in strategy can occur.

The design of a movement is a thought. The only effective tools that can be used to change a thought are other thoughts. Consequently, it is the redirecting and retraining of our thinking that will provide the means of escape from our monkey traps.

*   *   *   *   *

When most of us consider the nature of thinking, our opinions are usually based on some model or other which minimizes the role of conscious thought. The simplest and most common representation of this is to draw a circle as if it were a pie with a small wedge-shaped piece cut out of it. In most people's concepts, the small wedge would be labeled "conscious" and the rest of the pie labeled "unconscious." This would certainly seem to be a reasonable model, particularly with respect to issues like life-support maintenance (we don't usually think all that much about breathing and heart beats and digestion) and our attitudes concerning the whole murky and tangled mess of our behavioral motivations.

In practice, though, people seem to believe that this model of "conscious" intervention can be applied equally well to voluntary movement. The commonly held belief is that there is only a small part of the thought processes that cause movement that is conscious and reasoning. While it is clear that most of the mechanics of carrying out movement responses happens "below the level of consciousness" – one doesn't really direct all the details of each muscle's participation or non-participation in each aspect of each movement event (nor would we want to) – perhaps we should reevaluate our understanding of the relative "consciousness" of those decisions that direct us in activity.

Because Alexander's discoveries and techniques deal with the conscious and reasoning parts of us and our movements, if the realm of conscious guidance were as small as this model suggests, then the effect of Alexander's technique would be correspondingly small, and we would predict that we would see only limited changes in limited areas using Alexander's technique. But this prediction isn't consistent with the way F.M. presents his work, nor is it consistent with the kind of changes one observes in classes. In fact, the observed number of consciously directed changes is far larger than would be predicted if an "unconscious"-behavior-dominated model were true. Consequently, I sought an answer to account for my observations and the answer came to me one day, as I was teaching an Alexander workshop to a drama class at a junior high school in Portland, Oregon.

One of the students brought up this very problem by asking what was the difference between conscious and unconscious thought, and which of the two was larger and more important. To answer him, I drew a pie chart on the board with the label "conscious thought" in the small wedge-shaped piece, and with the rest of the pie labeled "unconscious." He told me that my drawing was the way he had been taught the mind was organized in science class, but, by the way I was talking about consciousness, it seemed that I made the conscious part of the pie much bigger.

I then explained to him: "The value of any model, like the pie chart, is to be able to express some larger, less comprehensible phenomenon in a simpler and more comprehensible way. Sometimes the process of reduction or evaluation used to create a model could contain an error and generate a false model. But this isn't a problem, because one always used a model by testing it against experimental findings. If a model were valid and useful, the experimental findings would agree with the model. If the model was invalid or not useful, the experimental findings would not agree with the results the model would predict. But even that would not be a problem, because one of the advantages of having a model in the first place is that when the observations derived experimentally no longer fit the model, you can change the model to fit the observations. More importantly, you can test a model by running different experiments using that model and comparing the results against the results predicted by the model. In other words, if the model that you are presently using either no longer fits the observations generated or is proving to be a handicap in your advancement, then you can change the model to a more advantageous one. As long as your past and future observations are consistent with the new model, you can keep it for as long as it proves useful. Therefore, with regard to conscious and unconscious thought, perhaps the pie chart diagram is an appropriate visual representation, but, as we have pointed out, with respect to the issue of the processes of directing yourself in activity, perhaps the sizes and values should be reversed. While it is clear that some very large portion of the mental processes that are required to perform a movement take place in parts of the brain that are below the level of consciousness and therefore cannot be considered to be "conscious", what concerns us most in Alexander's work is the nature of the thoughts that organize and direct us in activity and, because these kinds of thoughts take place in the associative and pre-motor regions of the cortex, they are certainly capable of being conscious and are therefore subject to change as a result of changing the ways in which we are thinking. If at least some portion of the directive thoughts we have are subject to change as a result of a change in the way we are thinking, then, perhaps, it is true that there are two categories of directive thought – "conscious" and "unconscious" – and perhaps the difference in size is so large that one of the two is much larger than the other. But, what if the larger of these two kinds of directive thought is actually conscious thought?" is what I said.

Or something like that.

It was at this point that my sponsor to the class cleared his throat and got my attention. Apparently I had gone into a twenty-minute discussion with myself that he felt was no longer appropriate to an introductory Alexander class for young teenagers. So I took off my mad professor persona and returned to the class and the fun we had been having earlier while learning about the Alexander Technique.

But I never forgot the implications of those comments.

WHAT IF the largest part of our directive thinking processes is actually "conscious" and therefore subject to change as a result of changing the way we think about ourselves, our activities, and the performance of them? Or if conscious directive thought isn't the largest part of the pie, WHAT IF the size of the piece that represents conscious directive thought is larger than we generally take it to be? After my monologue in the drama class, I began an experiment that I continue to this day.

Since that day, I have acted in my personal practice and taught in my classes AS IF the model of the relationship of "conscious" directive thought to "unconscious" directive thought could be represented by a pie chart with a single wedge, but one in which the largest part of the pie was "conscious" directive thought. I reasoned that if this model were true, then one would predict that most, if not all, of the decisions which underlie and generate specific movement behaviors are conscious and, hence, able to be articulated. If the decisions for these behaviors are knowable and able to be articulated, then these decisions and the behaviors that they cause would certainly be capable of being altered by Alexander's procedures.

If a student could be trained to redirect his thinking in a more constructive manner, then the mental power the student could bring to bear on his own problem would become an ally instead of an obstacle. Consequently, to prove or disprove this model, I set out to see how many times I could find a specific decision or thought which underlay a client's unusual movement behaviors. In the last thirty years, I have not found one unusual habit or movement behavior that could not be traced back to some very specific, conscious decisions.

*   *   *   *   *

The most common way to trace one of these underlying conscious thoughts is to talk with a student in class about where a particular behavior may have originated. Often the answers are absolutely intriguing. The most dramatic of these examples occurred once with a student from Washington, D.C.

While watching this particular student walk in his usual manner, two distortions became clear very quickly. First of all, the movement of his legs was very exaggerated and very high, almost as if he were trying to produce a "goose-step" with a bent leg. Secondly, instead of moving his legs in a straight-ahead manner, he moved both legs to the side 45 degrees as they came forward. In fact, his walk was one of the most bizarre, non-pathologic gaits I have ever observed. When I questioned him about why he walked in this way, he told me why – immediately and emphatically.

When he was at military school as a teen-ager, he kept hitting the heels of the student marching in front of him in close order drill. This led to him being beaten up afterwards by his classmates. No matter how often he tried to stop hitting the other cadet's heels, he couldn't. Moving his legs in the exaggerated and peculiar manner he had demonstrated in class was the only way he had ever found to avoid striking the heels of the person marching in front of him. He happily adopted this strange way of walking because, if he avoided striking the heels of his classmates, they avoided striking him.

We will have more to say about our marching soldier and his decisions, but for now, it is sufficient to note that, on initial observation, his pattern of leg movements was bizarre and inexplicable. With further investigation, based on an analysis of the decisions the marching student had made, the way he moved his legs was not only reasonable, it made sense and provided an elegant – well, not so elegant – solution to his dilemma.

I have also found in my investigations that the precipitating cause of a bizarre or exaggerated behavior does not have to be a specific solution for a specific event.

I once had a patient who had a horrendous problem with "tension." As we talked about in the last chapter, she really didn't have "tension." What she had was the habit of using tremendous amounts of muscular force in opposing directions constantly so that, even when she was lying still, it was very difficult for someone else to move her arms, legs, and neck because of the resistance caused by the stiffening effect of her residual efforts. This continuous pulling of her own muscles against herself was so strong and so constant that, at a very young age, she was suffering from fatigue and the pain of repetitive stress injuries even though her life was not very active.

I worked with her clinically as a Restructuring client for almost three months.[45] Although she would get great relief during her sessions, she did not show the kind of on-going improvement between sessions that is characteristic of Restructuring clients. During her re-examination after two months of work, I was explaining to her that when a client goes this long without significant improvement, I usually make a referral to someone else because it is clear by then that my work is not helping. I told her that I knew that there was some reason why my treatment techniques were not preventing the return of her pattern of using extreme amounts of muscular effort to "hold onto" her muscles, but I couldn't figure out what that reason was. I told her that until the cause of her holding onto her muscles could be found and eliminated, I didn't think she would get any better while under my care.

After I had told her once more that I couldn't figure out the unknown cause of her problem, I turned away to do another procedure. After my back was turned, I heard this tiny little voice, like a four-year-old's, say, "But if I let go, the world will fall apart."

Here was a movement behavior strategy based on decisions made by a very small girl when faced with the dynamics of a very dysfunctional family. At one point in her life (and, in further discussions, my patient was very eloquent when talking about this particular time in her life), events and circumstances were so threatening that the only thing she could think of to do to help was to tighten all of her muscles in order to help "hold things together".

When events in her life didn't work out well, she was convinced it was because she hadn't held on tight enough so afterwards she would hold onto herself even tighter. When things worked out in an acceptable way during the time she was doing this excessive "holding things together", she became convinced that they worked out so well only because of how she had tightened her muscles. Therefore, she decided she had a responsibility to herself (and to everyone else) to keep her muscles tightened, no matter what. Forty years later, these decisions

---

[45]   Restructuring is the name I have given to the clinical procedures I developed as a synthesis of various aspects of my training as both an Alexander teacher and a chiropractor. Although Restructuring derives its principles from both disciplines, the process of analysis, design, and application of treatment techniques used in Restructuring is unique to it. It is important to note, also, that Restructuring is a genuine therapy process in that it is something that is done by the therapist to the client to effect a change in the client while the Alexander Technique remains, at all times, educational. Although both procedures have proven beneficial to clients, in practice, I almost always keep them separate.

had created repetitive stress injuries and premature degeneration in her arms and spine, as well as movement distortions and general muscular inefficiency.

But, she kept doing them.

We will talk more about our marching cadet and our world-saving body-contractor, and why they persisted with their maladaptive behaviors, but, for now, it is only important to see that their behaviors came from their ideas. Their behaviors came from conscious thoughts that remained active and in place despite the passage of time and the changing of circumstances.

After having traced hundreds of such examples back to the specific decisions related to specific events prior to the creation of these movement behaviors, I have yet to find any behavior that I could not trace back to similar decision-making processes. Consequently, I feel quite confident that the appropriate and more useful model to represent the role of "conscious" directive thought to "unconscious" directive thought is a pie-shaped diagram in which the small wedge represents "unconscious" directive thought and the larger region represents directive thought that is "conscious".[46]

*   *   *   *   *

So, movements are caused by the contraction of muscles, and muscular contractions are caused by the sending of messages along the nerves to the muscles involved. These messages are called impulses in the peripheral nerves, but they are the sort of thing that we call thoughts in our brains. Once we understand that commands sent to the muscles originate as thoughts in the brain, then we have a way of finding out something about the thoughts which an individual has.

First of all, we must begin with a basic decision about the relationship between thought and movement. I believe that most, if not all, voluntary movement behaviors begin with a thought. In other words, the relation of thinking to movement is causal.

---

[46]   In class we make a distinction between three initial levels of consciousness: conscious, aware, and acknowledged. I believe that an extremely large number of our actions are conscious in the sense that they are "worked out" and deliberate. The percentage of these conscious decisions of which we are aware, however, is smaller. The percentage of the conscious actions of which we are aware that we are willing or able to acknowledge at any given time is smaller still. The fact that we may not be aware of an action, or the fact that we may still not be able to acknowledge an action of which we are aware does not make these actions any less reasoned and deliberate, and therefore any less "conscious".

From my point of view, therefore – unless there is a severe organic or behavioral condition present – for an action to be classified as less than "conscious", I would have to find an act or movement behavior for which no underlying conscious decision or decisions could be found. To date, I have never found any unusual habit or movement behavior that could not be traced back to these kinds of decisions.

For instance, if I am going to move in some way, I must first make a decision to move in that way. This decision then becomes organized into a strategy for movement, and the strategy becomes implemented as commands to the muscles involved. In this way it can be said that muscles are activated by thoughts. I believe (and I am quite confident that Alexander would agree) that if there is a voluntary movement, then there was a thought that preceded and directed it.

In other words, there is no such thing as an Immaculate Contraction.

For example, if you were to ask me to touch my ear, in order for me to do that I must carry out all of the mental operations involved. I must also decide which hand to use and which ear to touch. I must calculate the probable pathways of movement to follow. I must decide how much force to use, and so forth. I must give consent to do the action, or withhold consent and not do it. In other words, once I have decided that I will touch my ear, I must devise a mental strategy for carrying out that action.

How these strategies are devised and carried out is a topic well beyond the scope of our present efforts and could be the subject of a great deal of excellent research. There is one aspect of all this, however, which it would serve us well to pursue.

Frank Jones talked about the distinction between behavior that is public and behavior that is private. While all of a person's behavior involves both thought and movement; only the movement occurs in a public arena, can be perceived, and is therefore "knowable". In other words, it is only a person's movement that can be detected by our senses. Because a movement can be detected by someone's senses, it can be said to be public, and only those things that are public and perceivable can be known by others. Everything else is private.

While it is true that we can learn to make reasonable inferences about a person's thinking by analyzing their public behavior, the thinking itself remains private and unknowable. If this were not the case, then deception (self- and otherwise) would not be possible. However, because of the way our nervous system interfaces with our muscles, we can work backwards from our perceived public movement behavior to find out something about the private thinking processes that created that behavior.

While we cannot "know" what was going on in a person's private thinking behavior, we can "know" how they moved. By comparing stated intent with actual result, we can learn to gauge the relative effectiveness of each person in carrying out his intention. In a well-coordinated individual, there is a very high correlation between stated intention and actual performance. This individual experiences a tremendous freedom of choice in terms of responses and is better able to respond freshly and creatively to each circumstance as it presents itself.

In an individual with poor coordination, there is often a discrepancy between stated intention and actual performance. In most cases, these individuals move as if dominated by a practically irresistible response or pattern of responses to every circumstance, which either stereotypes the response pattern or interferes with a fresh response to each new stimulus. This is what leads to the very low correlation between actual performance and intent.

In either case, by analyzing the motion performed, I can come to some conclusions about the thoughts and strategies that created them. In other words, if it is true that "by their actions, ye shall know them," then it is also true that by the manner of their actions ye shall "know" something of their thinking.

For example, let us look again at my touching my ear.

Suppose I announce that I am going to touch my ear, I must then formulate my strategy for carrying out the action – which hand to use, which finger, which movement pathway to follow, how much force to use, etc. But then suppose that when I project the messages from my brain to the mechanisms involved, I raise my hand and touch my nose instead.

Because the degree of coordination in an individual is equal to the relative ability of that individual to conceive of an idea, and then to carry out that idea as conceived, if I touch my nose after announcing my intention to touch my ear, we know that one of four things is true about me and my action. Either I misrepresented my intention when I spoke, my coordination is seriously impaired, I have a great need for an anatomy lesson, or I changed my mind.

Notice that, at this point and without further investigation, we cannot know which is true. But, we can "know" that there is a discrepancy between my stated intention and the action that I carried out.

There is, however, no discrepancy between the action carried out and the messages projected from the brain. If I touched my nose, the messages projected from the brain to the mechanisms involved had to include the messages that made me touch my nose. In fact, in the absence of any pathologic condition, the muscles can only carry out the commands that they receive.

These commands create the implementation of the movement strategies conceived. While it is possible to change the messages projected to the muscles before they are sent out, there is no practical way to change them once they are sent. Because of this, we can trace a person's "thinking" back as far as the commands sent to the muscles.

*   *   *   *   *

Let us suppose, then, that in a lesson, a student is asked to begin walking without pulling his head back, and that the student agrees to do this. Then, if, as he actually begins to walk, he does pull his head back, we can only be certain that the commands to the muscles included the commands to pull his head back.

We cannot "know" with any certainty about the student's true intent or what the student was thinking. The student's thoughts are private and unknowable. But we can make some guesses about what the student's directive thinking was.

If the student's movement response to the intention of walking without pulling his head back was similar or identical to his habitual movement response in walking (a response that included the pulling back of his head), we can infer that his habitual patterns of directive guidance dominated his relatively weak desire to change his manner of use in walking. We cannot know, however, whether or not he really tried to change his "thinking". On the other hand, if the student was in the habit of pulling his head back as he began walking and on some occasion does not pull his head back, we can be sure that the directive thinking that generated his movement did, in fact, change from his usual manner of directive thought.

I remember one time I was teaching an introductory class and I asked a student to tell me out loud what she was intending to do as she tried to do on her own what she thought I had shown her. As she informed me she was going to move her head up, she pulled it back and down. As she told me she was going to let her body follow her head upward, allowing her stature to lengthen, she began to "collapse". The more she told me she was "thinking" about moving her head up and lengthening, the more she screwed herself down into the chair.

I urged her to continue for some time. I wanted to see if she would finally reach a point where this way of "moving up" would feel to her like she was being squashed. But, as she persisted in telling me what she was doing (and shrank), she became more and more pleased with herself and more and more confident that she was carrying out the "orders" she was speaking out loud. Finally she ran out of room to move downward onto herself and just stayed there, in the chair, forcefully held together like a compressed accordion, and just as pleased as punch because she felt so light and long and easy.[47]

Although this example may give us many interesting things to consider, there is something that we can "know" from this experience. In spite of her stated intentions, we can "know" that the commands that were going to her muscles were for her to pull her head back and press herself down.

How do we know this?

---

[47] By the way, the slump she created as a result of "moving up" in this fashion was quite different from the slump she created when sitting casually. Therefore, it is unlikely that this slump of "moving up" was simply an increase of effort in her habitual response as is often claimed and assumed in such cases.

Because it is public and we can see it. No matter what was going on in her head to create this outcome or to analyze it, we can know that the final strategy that she turned into commands and carried out involved this backward and downward movement because her muscles visibly moved her down into this distortion.

What we can't know is the private maze of strategies, intentions, concepts, commands, and counter-commands that turned her stated desire into a contradictory action. As teachers, we can, at best, only make conjectures about these things – and we often have to – in order to construct appropriate teaching strategies. There is no way, however, in which we can say that we know what the student was thinking. We can only know what is publicly available – the movement.

Now from the movement, we can work backwards to guess something of the commands that initiated the movement. From the commands, we can work backwards again to guess something of the final decisions that led to the commands. From the final decisions, we can guess something of the values and beliefs that influenced these decisions. With each backwards step, however, the variables increase, the connections become more tenuous, and the thinking becomes more private.

If the process of learning this work is a battle between being trapped by one's habitual movement responses (and the thinking processes that create these responses) on the one hand and being free to design appropriate responses at will on the other, I do not believe that this "battle" will ever be won on the basis of movement correction, reflex initiation, or postural change. I believe that it must be won on the basis of training the student how to think. If the student's thinking is sound, then satisfactory movement and conditions must follow.

Chapter 9

FEELINGS AND THE TIME LINE

THE LAST TOPIC we need to discuss from a physiological point of view before we look more closely at the specifics of Alexander's work is the whole issue of our feeling sense with regards to movement. Some of the most important and most difficult questions in this work have to do with the role of feelings with regard to our patterns of directive guidance.[48] Questions such as: "What do we mean by feelings with regard to movement? Are feelings in this sense the same as emotions? Do feelings make an effective tool for guidance? When do feelings occur?" And so forth.

The list of questions regarding feelings in this work is quite long.[49] Once again, the way in which these questions are answered will determine much of what you think the work is and how it is to be accomplished. What I propose to do in this chapter is present certain physiologic facts that serve as the basis for my own answers to these questions. As I go along, I will try to demonstrate the relevance of this information with respect to the work.

Like the chapter on muscles, the information may seem so technical that it may intimidate you. There is no need for any of this material to do that, even if you find yourself re-reading sections many times. Almost everyone has to read this kind of material many times and give it much thought before they can un-

---

[48] The discussion of the role of feelings and sensory appreciation in this work is very important, but extremely controversial. It would be inappropriate in this or any other introductory textbook to deal with the whole of this controversy in a manner befitting its importance, and I hope that the balance of the rest of my writings will address this discussion more fairly and completely. In this chapter, I intend to present the distillation of the argument with respect to the role of feelings in this work that makes the most sense to me. Because I will do this in a simple and straightforward manner, I anticipate that the presentation of this particular aspect of what I teach might serve as a target point for the rejection of this approach as a whole. While I respect one's right to reject this approach, I would ask anyone who is a strong proponent of any of the other points of view about the importance of the feeling sense in Alexander's work that they may suspend their final judgment about what is said now so that I may present a simple introductory argument here, and a more complete one elsewhere.

[49] In the discussion that follows, by "feeling" or "feelings", I will usually mean the feeling-sense interpretation of the raw data sent through the input mechanism. This usage of the term "feelings" should convey both the concept of the raw data and the impressions derived from that data. I will try to use the term "feeling sense" when referring to the data alone. In a similar way, the use of the term "movement" in this discussion is intended to refer to volitional movements: movements which we plan in response to stimuli.

derstand it. If you keep at it, however, I believe that when you are finished you will be well rewarded.

*   *   *   *   *

One way to look at how we are made is to see ourselves divided into two large divisions. In their book *Illustrated Physiology,* McNaught and Callander call these two large divisions "meta-systems". The first of these meta-systems, according to them, is called the Vegetative Meta-system. It is made up of the digestive, respiratory, excretory, transport, and endocrine systems. The function of the Vegetative System is to keep us alive. The second meta-system is called the Master Tissues. It is made up of the nervous system, skeleton, and musculature. The function of the Master Tissues is to receive information, analyze it, and formulate a response. In very simple terms, the Vegetative Meta-system creates and sustains life, and the Master Tissues carry the Vegetative Meta-system around to acquire the resources it requires and generally keep it out of harm's way.

Clearly, of the two meta-systems, the one most involved with the Alexander Technique is the Master Tissues. We have already talked about the muscles and bones. It is time now to look more closely at the nervous system to see if we can shed some more light on the role of feelings with respect to guiding movements.

*   *   *   *   *

There are many ways to think of the nervous system. One of the more useful ways is to think of it in terms of how it performs its functions. If we focus in on how the Central Nervous System deals with messages and responses, a very valuable way of looking at the nervous system presents itself.

In this respect, the nervous system can be thought of as consisting of three parts:

INPUT → PROCESSING → OUTPUT

This includes a part for taking in information (Input), a part for correlating that information and formulating a response (Processing), and a part for carrying these response commands to the end organs, usually muscles, which will make the response (Output).

We've already talked a little about the last two parts of this model in the preceding chapter. As we saw, the "brain" processes the information available to it, makes a decision about what to do, and then sends commands to the muscles to be carried out. Except in very special circumstances, once the commands reach the motor cortex of the brain the action to be carried out cannot be changed. You can send a second counteractive command very soon after, but the initial action itself cannot be changed. Therefore, if we are ever going to have an effect on changing our actions, the change must take place in our manner of processing commands.

But what about the parts of our nervous system which provide input?

What role does the Input portion of our model play in the processing of commands?

*   *   *   *   *

When we think of the mechanisms of input in our nervous system, we most often think of the five senses: sight, taste, sound, smell, and touch. All of these senses deal predominantly with information that is external to us. They provide a means of understanding something about the world in which we find ourselves.

The last of these senses – touch – has a second role as well. The mechanisms by which we are able to sense a great deal of information about those things with which we come into contact in the outside world is very similar to the mechanisms that we use to come into contact with ourselves. This process of self-sensing is called proprioception.

There are many different kinds of proprioception. Through proprioception, we are able to sense hot and cold within us. We are able to distinguish between light and heavy touch. We are able to feel pain. We are able to sense pressure at joints. We are able to detect the amount of contraction or stretching in our muscles, and so forth.

The proprioceptive sense that seems to be of the most interest to students of Alexander is the kinesthetic sense. For the most part, the popular usage of this term has become so generalized and misapplied that it is no longer technically accurate. Strictly speaking, kinesthesia is actually a sub-part of what is called the position sense.[50] The position sense is made up of two parts: the static position recognition sense and kinesthesia.

The static position recognition sense is that sense which registers the part-to-part relationships of bones to one another at the joints. In his paper "Re-orientation of the View Point upon the Study of Anatomy" (portions of which occur as an appendix in Alexander's fourth book), Dr. Mungo Douglas tells us that the function of muscle is twofold: "to perform movements of parts about

---

[50] Guyton, Arthur C., *Textbook of Medical Physiology*. 6th edition, W. B. Saunders Company, Philadelphia, London, and Toronto, p. 607.

joints and [to] maintain relations of parts to parts."[51] The static position recognition sense is the feeling sense that informs us about the second of these two functions: the part-to-part relationship of bones to bones at the joints. Kinesthesia, on the other hand, merely informs us about the rate at which any given movement is performed. It will be seen from this that, technically, the feeling sense we are most interested in improving is not our kinesthesia but our static position recognition sense.

The easiest way to identify and understand this static position recognition sense is to take one of your hands and hold it back behind your head so that none of your fingers are touching one another or anything else. Then make a concerted effort to wiggle your fingers in such a way that you might confuse yourself about where your fingers are in relation to one another. Then, after a little while, stop.

If you will continue to hold your fingers "still," after a few moments you should begin to develop a kind of "picture" of how your fingers are arranged with respect to one another. For most people, in a very short time, it is almost as though they can "see" their fingers. This ability to sense the relationships of the joints of your fingers without looking at them is the static position recognition sense (although most people refer to it as the kinesthetic sense). The reason why this kind of feeling sense has such a strong visual component is believed to be that it shares common neural pathways with the vision pathways in our brain.

After my students have done this little exercise, I then challenge them to do the same sort of thing in trying to "sense" where their heads are in relation to their bodies. In this experiment, wiggling and shaking of your head is optional. But, even without shaking your head, everyone to some degree should be able to "see" the relationship of his or her head and neck in just the same sort of way as you were able to "see" your fingers. When one is first starting, this image of your head is not usually so clear as the image of your fingers, but it can be developed with time and practice.

*   *   *   *   *

There are a number of other facts about the feeling senses that make up the input portion of our nervous system model and that have great importance in assigning a value and a role to the use of these feeling senses in guiding our movements.

---

[51]   Jones, Frank Pierce, *Freedom To Change,* Mouritz, 1997, London, p. 60. It is interesting to note that Alexander, in quoting Douglas in Appendix C of his fourth book, prefers the phrasing Douglas uses in the next sentence: "the function of muscles is twofold: namely, movement of parts about joints, and directive of part to part." Alexander, F. Matthias, *The Universal Constant in Living.* Mouritz, London, 2000, p. 198.

First of all, sensory organs, like muscles and other nerves, have a threshold for becoming active. In other words, a certain amount of stimulus is required before the sensory organ will fire. It's a little like tickling someone who doesn't want to admit that he is ticklish. As you start tickling your victim, he may be able to hold still. If you keep it up, however, eventually he won't be able to control himself any longer and may start laughing or squirming or both.

In a similar way, there is a build-up of stimulation at one (and often more) of the sensory receptor organs until the threshold amount is reached. The sensory organ then sends off a message back to the brain that it is being tickled or stretched or compressed or made hot or hurt or whatever the particular job of reporting might be for that particular sensor. If this threshold limit is not reached, the sensor remains "silent" and no information is sent to the brain.

The second thing to remember about the feeling sense is that there is a tremendous amount of information going into the processing part of the central nervous system all of the time. In their *Color Atlas of Physiology,* Depopoulos and Ibernagl claim that the number of bits of information which reaches the thalamus (a kind of central switch board to the higher centers of the brain) is about one billion bits of information each second, every second. The thalamus, in turn, passes along for recognition less than a hundred of these bits each second – and herein lays the basis for many misunderstandings in the work.

Often in this work, people get the impression that their teachers are saying that their feelings are unreliable. Sometimes, unfortunately, this is because that is precisely what their teachers tell them. Now, there is a very important issue that has to do with feeling-sense impressions and reliability, but it is not true that the "feelings (themselves) are unreliable."

The information being brought to the brain from our input mechanism – the feeling sense – is always accurate and reliable. Our feeling sense is always reliable because this kind of "feeling" is just the raw data going into the brain for processing. In the absence of disease or damage to the sensory mechanism, there can be no unreliability of the feeling sense. It is what we do with this accurate data that leads to unreliability of interpretation. It is the rules that we use to assign meaning to the data and the rules we use to determine which hundred pieces of information we will pay attention to each second and which nine hundred ninety-nine million, nine hundred ninety-nine thousand, nine hundred bits we will throw away that will determine much of what we experience.

*   *   *   *   *

The first rule that is observed in "deciding" which bits of information to keep and which to ignore is based on survival. Information that enhances our chances of survival has the highest priority.

For instance, if we have hurt ourselves, the information passes through the system quickly along the fastest nerves to make us aware of a problem to which we may need to respond. Similarly, as we swim along underwater, the relative need for another breath created by the oxygen debt of our activity is increasingly apparent. So, the first rule of attention can be summarized as: any information that relates directly to the survival and immediate well-being of our mechanism has a higher priority than any other information.

The second rule for excluding information is that any pattern of information that is constant and unchanging is more likely to be ignored. The reasons for this are easy to understand.

In the first place, the amount of information about any particular region sent to the brain is greatest at the moment of change – the point at which the threshold of the greatest amount of sensor distortion is reached or exceeded. The importance of this information begins to diminish after that point in time. As the system becomes accustomed to the stimuli provided by a particular condition, the persistence of the stimuli creates a context in which the relative importance of the stimuli diminishes. In other words, the information that stays unchanged is the information most likely to drop out of our attention. Therefore, one is much more likely to register change than stasis.

In a similar way, to the degree we are able to direct our attention, we are able to shape the information we perceive. Our concepts create certain kinds of filters that also seem to be in operation in determining which bits of information are saved and which are discarded. That is, to some degree, we eliminate some information on the basis of disinterest or conflict, and pass along other information that conforms to our beliefs. Anyone who has ever been in an Alexander class in which students' impressions are solicited has probably seen this kind of denial at work.

*   *   *   *   *

The most striking of this kind of experience has happened to me three times in my teaching career. On these occasions I have been working with someone on the activity of standing up from a chair. On each of these occasions, each student – after having left the chair and supporting himself on his feet – has argued with me vigorously about whether or not he was standing.

During the first incident, I was working with a student in my customary manner. All was going well until I asked him to stand. Throughout the entire movement from seated to standing, major transformations took place throughout his entire body. Once he had reached an easy and upright condition on his feet, he was hardly recognizable as the same person.

While I'm sure he got a tremendous surprise during this experience, I got an even bigger one when I asked him what he noticed about himself as he was standing there. The student assured me that he was not standing at all! When I casually remarked that he looked like he was standing to me, he told me that he didn't care what it looked like – he wasn't standing. When I asked him directly if he was standing, he told me, "Of course not. I can't stand like this!"

I realized, of course, that what was really happening was that, as a result of having moved in this new way, the feeling-sense data he was receiving from his input system was so different that he couldn't match what he was experiencing with what he expected to feel in carrying out the movement of standing. In other words, the feelings he had experienced and was experiencing did not match the feelings he had had previously while standing and so he was having trouble applying the "label" of "standing" to his new experience.

This had often happened in lessons before. What surprised me this time was that no amount of questioning or coaxing on my part could elicit any response from him except a firm and definite denial that he was standing. When I asked him what he was doing if he was not seated or standing, he said, "I don't know, but I'm not standing."

Once I became convinced that the student was not joking, I allowed the argument to go on to see how long he would persist in his claim that he was not standing. When I asked him about what he had felt as he moved, he could talk about the feeling sense associated with some, but not all, of the events that took place as he came up out of the chair. When I asked him if he was still seated, he told me he was not. When I asked him if he had to look up at me to see my face when he was seated, he said, "Yes." When I asked him if he was looking up to see my face now, he replied, "No, I'm looking down at you." When I asked him if he was standing, he said, "No, I am not!"

I even invited the other members of the class to confirm or deny my contention that the student was standing. Not only did he not believe his classmates when they told him he was standing, he argued with them as well, turning bright red from the exertion. After twenty minutes, it became clear to me that the argument was not going to stop of its own accord, so I asked the student to do what he needed to do to stand.

He promptly sat down and stood up again, this time more in accordance with his habitual manner of standing. I then asked him if he was standing and he said that he was. On questioning, however, he could not tell me what was significantly different about what he had been doing moments before and what he was doing now. He could not tell me what he had done to change from his previously unidentified condition to standing, nor would he be convinced that he had been standing before.

On the second occasion that this same kind of denial occurred, I allowed the arguing to go on only long enough for the rest of the class to be satisfied that their classmate was serious about his denial and that his carrying on about not standing was a demonstration of great internal distress and not a practical joke.

I reminded him of the first time this had happened and asked him if he remembered the story. He said that he did. When I asked him if he thought that story was in any way relevant, he replied, "I don't know. I just know that I am not standing. I can't stand like this!" When I asked him to do what he would need to do to stand, rather than sitting down again and popping up again as the other student had done, he merely collapsed into a much more familiar condition of slumping, breathed a heavy sigh of relief and announced, "Now! Now I am standing!"[52]

In both cases, the students had to have received from their feeling senses information about performing the act of standing. They must have had pressure on their feet. They must have felt the absence of pressure on their buttocks and the backs of their legs as they lifted up off of their chairs. They must have received feeling-sense information about the multiple changes in degree of joint angulations, and rate of change consistent with the motion that they performed. But, because this act (and the feelings generated by it) was so different from their usual way of standing, these sensations were edited out to some degree – at least by interpretation – and those sensations which did get through were subjected to the most intense form of denial and re-interpretation.

The distress and conflict which each student felt was genuine. The only difference between what they experienced and what most other people experience in a lesson is one of degree. Still, their capacity for separating out unwanted bits of information and for denying inconsistent information remained powerful and dominant in spite of everything the rest of us said. In fact, I later joked in class with the second student about that particular experience to make a point. We all joked and laughed and enjoyed the relevance of the story to the question we were discussing, but, as I started to continue on with the next part of the lecture, the student said softly, "But I wasn't standing."

Part of what lies at the heart of this denial is the reliance we make upon our feelings to act as a kind of anchor for our impressions about ourselves. We use our interpretations of our feeling sense to judge our condition, to evaluate our performance, and to act as a model for projected future performances. In fact, much of the teaching that is done in the performing arts and in athletics is based on developing the ability to reproduce a "feeling" in order to reproduce a sound, a movement, or a stroke.

This process of organizing responses to match a *"feeling"* as a means of directive guidance is the one that Alexander believed to be operative in himself when he began his investigation and that he believed to be nearly universal. He also, at one point, believed his reliance upon untrustworthy feelings for guidance

---

[52] The most recent occurrence of this phenomenon followed the same pattern as the second event. As soon as the student was able to slump in a familiar way, the student agreed with the claim that he was standing.

was the source of his difficulties and that this untrustworthiness of feelings was THE stumbling block that prevented him from being able to change the use of himself in activity. Like many others who came after him, he then sought to retrain this manner of guidance to make it reliable once more. But, unlike most of them, he rejected seeking the guidance of even a trustworthy feeling sense because of its impracticality and procedural irrelevance.[53]

In fact, if reliance upon feeling as a valuable and reliable form of guidance were to be used foundationally in this work, two things would have to be true. In the first place, our "feelings" would have to reflect all of the information coming in as well as be free from the imperfections of misinterpretation and, thereby, be unchanging in value. Secondly, feelings would have to "exist" earlier in time than the movements that create them. As we shall see, neither one of these conditions is ever likely to be true.

*   *   *   *   *

As we have seen above, the probability of those bits of information that get through to our planning centers being free from the imperfection of editing is very low. And once the information gets to our planning centers, it is further compromised by the belief structures that rule there. We usually have too much investment in what we think is right to pay attention to the information coming in without censorship. Even if we had complete integrity with regard to what we perceived and even if we could somehow organize ourselves to take in meaningfully all of the information from the entire Input mechanism, we could never-never-never-never-never-never-never-ever meet the second half of this first requirement because feelings are not absolute!

Probably the simplest demonstration of the non-absolute nature of our feeling sense is a little experiment you can carry out at home. Take three bowls and place them in front of you on a table. Fill the first bowl with water that is very hot, but not so hot that it is dangerous or uncomfortable. Fill the third bowl with water that is very cold (again taking care to avoid dangerous extremes). Fill the middle bowl with room temperature water.

Now carefully place one hand in the hot-water bowl and the other hand in the cold-water bowl. Then, after a little while, place both hands in the middle bowl at the same time.

If feelings worked in an absolute rather than a relative way, we would expect you to experience the temperature of the water in the middle bowl as being one temperature somewhere in between the two extreme temperatures of the outer bowl. What actually happens in almost every case, is that putting both hands in the middle bowl at the same time gives the individual the impression that the

---

[53] For a more complete discussion, see Volume II of *The Alexander Commentaries*.

water in the middle bowl has two different temperatures! The hand that was in the hot water "tells" you that the water in the middle bowl is cold and the hand that was in the cold water "tells" you that the water in the middle bowl is hot.

In other words, although both hands are experiencing the same temperature, the water temperature is "interpreted" differently because of the differences in the "pathway" of experience taken by each separate hand. The conditions present prior to the placing of each hand in the middle bowl are different, the relative changes in temperature are different, and, consequently, the person in the experiment "registers" the difference of each relative change separately.

The same kind of thing can also happen with respect to the static position recognition sense.

Often when teaching a beginning class, at least one of the students will exhibit the movement behavior of pulling his head and body very far backward and down while walking, creating a very compressed posture with the appearance of "falling" to the rear as he walks. When the teacher works with such students and begins to help them prevent this excessive backward movement, they will then walk around with a lessened backward slump. Inevitably, when questioned about what they are feeling, however, they will reply that the teacher has tipped them overly forward. Many will claim that they are actually falling forward, and, occasionally, the sensation of "falling forward" will be so pronounced that they will refuse to walk – in spite of the fact that they can still be clearly seen by the other students in the class to be leaning backwards still!

In cases like this, these students have been leaning backwards while walking for so long that it has come to feel familiar to them. In fact, it often comes to feel "normal". If they possessed an absolute feeling sense, they would describe their way of walking before the teacher works with them as "pressed very far backwards" or something like that, but they don't ordinarily do this. If they say anything, it is usually just to agree that they are walking their usual way or, sometimes, they will even claim they are walking normally.

If their feeling sense were absolute, we would predict that after the teacher has worked with them they would report something like, "I feel as though I am walking in a manner that is less compressed backwards" or "I seem to be leaning backwards less as I walk" or some such. But they don't! "I feel like you are tipping me right onto my nose!" is a comment I have heard more than once.

We will talk a great deal about the importance of this phenomenon later, but for now it is only important to see that feelings are not absolute.

*   *   *   *   *

One of the clear characteristics about the way in which we respond to stimuli and carry out behavior in real life is that it seems continuous. With regard to the process of making any one particular movement, however, there seem to be four different kinds of activity involved.

First of all, there is the movement itself. Secondly, there is the feeling associated with the movement. Thirdly, there is the process of planning the movement. And, lastly, there is the "thinking" process that is involved in projecting the commands created by the planning for the purpose of directing the movement. In other words, by "thinking," I mean the actual process by which we project the messages from the brain to the mechanisms involved. Because of the continuous nature of our movements and interactions, these four aspects of the performance of a given movement can be thought of as appearing in the same cycle in this fashion:

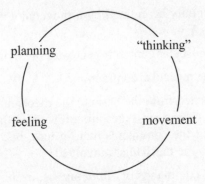

When I speak of creating a time line, I mean the breaking of this cycle for the purpose of placing these four aspects of a given, specific, single movement into a straight line by which the causal relationships of each of these aspects is kept intact with regard to the performance of that specific movement. In other words, the time line represents what would happen if one were to cut this seemingly continuous circle and stretch it out into a single line of events with respect to one movement.

When considering the causal relationships of a single movement, I believe that it is important to start with the movement itself. By doing that, one can then look at the causal impact of the temporal relationships involved.

When we were looking at what caused feeling-sense input, we saw that it was movement that caused different sensory receptors to fire at different times. Without the movement, these receptors would not be activated. In this way, it can be seen that the predominant experience that reaches us with regard to any movement is the sense of change created by the successive firings of different sensory receptors. Because these firings were caused by the movement, the "feeling" of a given movement is engendered by the movement itself and hence, can happen only after the movement has taken place.

Even in the case of continuous movement, when one has the experience of "feeling the movement while it is taking place", the movement that one is feeling is actually a movement which preceded the movement occurring in the present moment. It is only the speed with which the information is transmitted in the presence of the continuation of similar motion that creates the illusion of feeling a movement while it is taking place.

Feelings, therefore, are history.

They take place only as a result of the distortions of the sensory organs caused by a movement. Therefore, in any meaningful time line, feelings with regard to the movement that has created them can only happen after the movement has taken place.

But, if feelings can only be created by a movement, what creates the movement?

As we have seen, muscular contraction creates the movement.

But what creates the muscular contraction?

The messages projected from the brain to the mechanisms involved create the muscular contractions. These messages are initiated by the process I call "thinking" – the projection of the commands that, in turn, become the messages projected from the brain to the mechanism involved.

The creation of the commands of "thinking" is, in this point of view, a function of planning. In planning, we formulate strategies as a response to the stimulus that presently has, at least part, of our attention. In turn, we translate these strategies into the commands of "thinking" and these projected commands are turned into our specific movement response by the subordinate controls of the body.

When seen in this way, it is clear that the planning which creates the commands precedes the "thinking" or projection of those commands. It is the process of projecting those commands that directly precedes the messages being sent from the brain to the mechanism involved. It is the messages from the brain to the mechanisms involved that precede the movement; in fact, the movement is determined by these messages. The movement, in turn, distorts the sense organs and causes them to fire. It is the firing of the sense organs that precedes and creates the feeling-sense information of the movement that will later be interpreted by us as a feeling. Consequently, the feelings caused by the movement and the feeling of movement itself can happen only after the movement has occurred.

As a result of this reasoning, I cut the circle listed above at nine o'clock. By moving clockwise around the circle, this creates the following formula for a time line with respect to any given movement:

$$P \rightarrow \text{``t''} \rightarrow M \rightarrow F$$

where P (planning) is the creation of the protocol to be followed in the performance of a given activity, "t" ("thinking") is the projection of the directions required to create the protocol, M (movement) is the realization of the protocol, and F (feeling) is the product of the movement.

When one understands these causal relationships in the time line, one immediately understands the impossibility of using feelings – trustworthy or otherwise – as the source of directive guidance for any particular movement. Feelings can only happen after a movement. You can't use something that hasn't happened yet to create itself. But, in class, we see students try to use this strategy all the time.

A student who is at that point in a lesson where it is appropriate to begin walking will often remain standing still long after the teacher has given the suggestion to move. On questioning, the student will often reveal that he was trying to "feel" that smooth sense of gliding which he had had in a previous lesson BEFORE he starts to move. He is convinced that that particular feeling is what he wants and he will wait until it happens before he begins to walk. Consequently, he will stand rooted to that spot forever (or at least until the teacher devises a way to get him to move).

Even though the act of standing still has no chance to create the feeling he desires, a student will persist in this behavior, convinced that he should wait until he gets that feeling back before he begins to move. The one thing the student won't do to get back the feeling of walking that he liked again is to begin walking – the only procedure that has a chance to produce the effect he desires.

*   *   *   *   *

When Alexander admitted that he had not thought out how he directed himself in activity, he decided that he relied on his feelings to guide himself. He had no proof of this. It was just his supposition.

He then set out on what seemed to him to be a reasonable course of action to make this means of guidance trustworthy again. He found, to his surprise, that this process of guidance didn't work.

As we follow his story of discovery further in the chapter entitled "Evolution of a Technique,"[54] we see that once Alexander begins to investigate how he directs himself in activity he quickly abandons efforts to make his feelings a trustworthy source of guidance. He abandoned these efforts because his feelings did not prove to be either the actual source of his directive guidance or the cause of his misdirection.

---

[54]   This is the first chapter of Alexander's third book, *The Use of the Self*.

Feelings are, without a doubt, an important tool to use in judging the quality of a past performance, and this is a task for which they are well suited. A past performance is a thing of history, just as feelings are history themselves. When Alexander sought to find a way to change his responses in the on-going present, however, he found that feelings, as creatures of the past, contained neither predictive value nor future imperatives. He found that his responses were organized in a way that was not dependent upon feelings but were governed by other things instead. After learning what these other things were and how they worked, he devised mental disciplines for retraining his thinking so that his responses could be raised to a constructive, conscious, reasoned level of planning and execution.

It is these mental disciplines for retraining a person's thinking which create the value that we seek in Alexander's work today. These are the tools that he created and employed to fashion himself into the person of achievement and control which he became and which we choose to emulate. As far as the use of trustworthy feelings is concerned, Marjory Barlow tells us what Alexander ultimately thought about the value of even trustworthy feelings when she reports him as saying: "The time will come when you will be able to trust your feeling; when that time comes (however) you won't want to (use it) because you'll have something so much more reliable which will take you into the sort of change you want."[55] From his own story it is clear that Alexander thought that the mental disciplines that he devised as his technique would be preferable to the employment of even a trustworthy sensory guidance.

If we are ever to complete our task successfully, if we are ever to do what Alexander did, then we must find out about those mental disciplines that Alexander thought we would prefer to use. We must come to understand what they are, how they came about, how they operate, and how we can use them for our own benefit.

Having learned the nature and role of feelings with regard to the process of directive guidance, we must put aside our fascination with the past and look ahead to how we can shape our futures. We must recognize the effort to retrain our feelings as the key to reliable guidance for the fascinating by-path that it is, and learn to accept that there are processes for changing our manner of directive guidance that will make the accurate retraining of our feelings unavoidable. We must continue to seek those processes which will retrain our manner of thinking and which will provide a basis for constructive change in our lives.

In order to do this effectively, however, we must first come to understand the true nature of the transactions involved in the problem that Alexander solved: the problem that troubles us still.

---

[55] Barlow, Marjory, "The Essence of F.M.'s Teaching". *The Alexander Journal*, Number 15, Autumn 1997, p. 6.

THE REAL SOURCE
OF THE PROBLEM

Chapter 10

OUR HABITUAL PATTERNS
OF DIRECTIVE GUIDANCE

WHEN ALEXANDER began looking at what he used to direct his own use, he first believed that he relied upon his feelings as his source of direction. He wrote, "I had never thought of how I directed the use of myself, but that I used myself habitually in the way *that felt natural* to me. In other words, I, like everyone else, (believed that I) depended upon 'feeling' for the direction of my use."[56] When he tried to retrain the trustworthiness of this process of direction, he gradually came to see that the actual source of guidance within him was something else entirely. Consequently, what he had to learn in order to make changes in the use of himself in activity changed as well.

Rather than merely having to recalibrate the existing mechanism that he believed to be the source of his guidance, he had to discover the actual nature of how he sent himself into activity. He came to see that his habitual patterns of responses to stimuli were not entities in themselves but the direct results of commands that he was constantly giving to himself. These commands, based on his values and beliefs, became the practically irresistible basis for all of his responses.

In a similar way, we, too, have fixed convictions about who and what we are and how it is that we work best. We have turned these convictions into commands which we project all the time, but particularly as we enter into movement. It is not so much that we have ways of responding to stimuli that are fixed and habitual, but that we have made decisions that are fixed and habitual about how we should respond to stimuli. The commands associated with those decisions are the ones that we habitually invoke. To the outside observer, our public behavior appears to be habits of movement, but it is clear from our understanding of the relationship between movement and thought that these habitual-seeming movement behavior patterns are merely the products of certain "habits" of thought.

*   *   *   *   *

For most of us, there are certain stereotyped thoughts that precede and accompany every movement. These thoughts can occur on many levels. They range from the simple conviction we may have about what is required to initiate every

---

[56] Alexander, F.M., *The Use of the Self.* Gollancz, London, 1985, p. 35.

movement to terse articulations of rules to live by to the most intricate of task-specific protocols such as dancing or surgery. These thoughts, these practical expressions of our beliefs and values, become the commands that generate the physical-plane realization of our beliefs.

If we are going to move, there has to be both planning and "thinking" which precede the movement. When we perform acts that are common and familiar, we call upon the storehouse of information we have developed with regard to movement. We call forth protocols that we have used before. Rather than going through the "hassle" of "re-inventing the wheel" each time we move, we tend to generalize circumstances as much as possible in order to label the task in some familiar way. This allows us to re-issue the commands of previous protocols "automatically" with only a superficial sense of their appropriateness in a given situation.

The commands from previous protocols are like the initial programming in computer software. Certain set values and conditions are built into the starting point of each piece of software. This is called the default setting. If you use your computer without making any changes in the programming, the computer will carry out its tasks based on these default rules. Similarly, if you begin an activity or a movement without making any changes in the commands that have been issued previously, these commands remain active and in place and the responses you make now will be the same as your previous responses because every movement performed has a one-to-one correspondence to the commands which create it.

We tend to call repeatedly upon these commands from previous protocols in every activity. They often determine the nature and quality of our movements. They are the stuff with which we shape ourselves if not our lives. They are always in place. They are always active. It is only with the greatest of disciplined efforts that we can learn to escape their domination. We can think of these commands from previous protocols, from which we draw the design of our common responses, as our habitual patterns of directive guidance.

*   *   *   *   *

For the most part, the development of these habitual patterns of directive guidance occurs without notice. One of the major reasons for this is that many of these decisions and the commands that they engender occur at a very early age.

I remember sitting in the Dallas airport many years ago, waiting for my flight, and watching an infant who was lying on his back in an infant carrier. As I watched, I was fascinated by the movement of his legs. His left leg was curled around in that circular progression of joints so typical of young babies as he played with his foot with both hands. What made his behavior so fascinating was that, at the same time, his right leg was being held out to the side, in a straight line, at a 45 degree angle up and out from his hip. He was repeatedly snapping his lower leg into a near-perfect point, like a ballet dancer, alternating from a straight leg to a fully flexed knee.

Here was this young boy with one leg in a nearly perfect, motionless but continuous circle and the other leg in a nearly perfect, but constantly changing and repeating, series of angles and lines.

I watched him for a while to see how long this would continue. As with any infant, there would be times when his attention would be caught up in the noises around him, but, for the most part, he performed this activity for over fifteen minutes before curiosity led me to interview his mother. I'll never forget what she said.

"Moving like that seems to be his favorite thing to do. He'll just sit and do it for hours. I don't know why he does it. It just seems like one day he decided that that was what he wanted to do, and he's done it ever since. We've tried to get him to stop. We've even tried to get him to change legs, but he's made up his mind that this is the way to do it and so, do it he does."

I don't have any better idea why he does this behavior than his mother did. But I believe that somehow, somewhere, he got excited about moving his legs in this way and sent out the commands required to do it. And he continued to send them out. This behavior and the increasingly familiar feelings they generated had now come to play a central part in his world. They will probably play a central role in his world for a long time to come.

I would have loved to have been able to watch this child periodically over the next twenty years to watch what progression of behavior, if any, occurred as a result of this favorite way of moving. I would have loved to see what became of this behavior. I would have loved to see whether it remained overt or whether it became modified to something more acceptable or whether it served as his identifying choreographic style as a world famous dancer or whether it just got dropped altogether.

I don't know why he decided to behave this way, but I am sure that he decided to do it. I am also sure that this movement behavior will remain enforced until he decides to change it.

*   *   *   *   *

All movement behavior comes from the commands that implement the strategies required to bring to life the ideas generated during the planning stage. Once used, these movement behaviors – through increasing familiarity – have a strong tendency to be repeated. The sources of these ideas, however, are not always as mysterious as with our little Texan.

The most commonly cited source of movement ideas for young people is imitation of the movement patterns of others. For the many reasons involved, a person may adopt any of a number of movement characteristics from any of a number of people.

I know that in my own case, years ago I saw a picture of Bob Cousy[57] standing with a basketball resting on his hip. To balance this action, his hip was slung out to the side and his body appeared to be dropped down into his other hip. Anyone who knows this picture and who saw me standing casually at a certain point in my life (with or without a basketball) would have readily seen that this picture, along with a dash of hero worship, provided the basis for my "habitual" stance.

And the source of our imitation does not have to be famous people or unusual actions.

One day I was walking in Lincoln, Nebraska, with my best friend. As we were walking north on Thirteenth Street, we saw coming towards us a boy and his parents. They were walking three abreast with the young boy in the middle, holding his parents' hands. The mother, standing to the boy's right, walked with a characteristic swinging of her stiffened right leg in a wide arc. The father, on the boy's left, walked with a very strong collapse into his left leg and hip. The boy, walking between them and keeping in perfect step with each parent, had the same exact pronounced swing of his right leg and the same exact marked collapse on his left.

Both my friend and I were convinced that the other had arranged this piece of street theatre as a kind of practical joke. We couldn't believe that any kind of behavior that was that clear and obvious a demonstration of the principles of imitation could be true. I have since seen at least five other similar familial trios, but never one so striking as that first time.

And not all of a young child's decisions are based on simple imitation.

Most of the unusual behaviors that I see in my classes come from the strategies devised to respond to some problem in the real world. As we will point out again later, these strategies are sometimes in response to mistaken perceptions, but, quite often, they represent solutions to problems; solutions that can be seen as nothing less than brilliant.

---

[57]   Bob Cousy was a basketball player who played for Holy Cross and the Boston Celtics. Cousy is credited with elevating the importance of dribbling and passing skills in professional basketball, and was the first superstar of the Celtic dynasty.

A number of years ago, some of my colleagues brought their very young daughter to see me in my clinic to consult with me about an abnormality that had appeared in her walking gait. It seemed that with each step of her left leg there was an added motion of her upper leg outward which was not present when she moved her right leg. I no longer remember what made me think of it, but I suddenly remembered where I had seen her use this motion before. To test my theory, I took the little girl out to a nearby set of stairs and asked her to climb up them.

When I let her go up on the left side of the stairs, she went up them easily. She would lift her left thigh up, place her left knee on the next tread, and push herself up to the next level. When I forced her to move to the right side of the stairway, she hesitated. When I forced her to begin her climb with her right leg, she was unable to figure out a way to go up the stairs at all.

For her, the process of "going upstairs" was something that was performed by getting as far to the left of the staircase as possible, getting your left knee over the tread, and wedging yourself up with your knee. On the face of it, her response seems like fairly bizarre behavior, but, with a little more information, it can be seen for the clever solution that it was.

This little girl and her parents lived in a beautiful home that had a stairway near the front door. The most striking aspect of this stairway was that it was a spiral stairway that turned to the left as you faced it from below. Because of the space in which it was built, the top of the step nearer to the axis of the stairway was a considerably shorter distance for a little person to cover than the much larger right side of the stairway. For this reason, beginning the process of "going upstairs" with the left leg on the left side of the stairway was the most efficient pathway to choose. Therefore, the strategy that made the "most sense" on this little girl's "most significant" stairway was for her to go up the stairs on the left side using her left side first.

Brilliant!

The problem in her walking gait was caused by generalizing this stair climbing strategy to the use of her legs in walking. The movement which seemed odd and out of place as she walked was actually a very small firing of the outside muscles of her left hip as she began to move her left leg in walking. This movement was also, of course, the very first part of the movement required to put her left knee up on the next step during the process of "going upstairs".

It was as though she had reasoned out that if moving her left leg outward to go up stairs was so successful, maybe she should include that outward movement every time she moved her left leg. As she got tall enough to walk up and down stairs easily, she developed a different strategy for performing this important, liberating task. The whole of her previous strategy for climbing up the stairs on hands and knees became less important, but one could still easily see a remnant of that strategy in the distortion of her walking gait.

*   *   *   *   *

Similarly, if there are thoughts or strategies that have worked for you in the past – or have seemed to work for you in the past – you will tend to use them again and again.

The most predictable example of this in sports is that of the baseball player who during a turn at bat adjusted his cap, stepped up to the plate, tapped the plate once, took two short practice swings, and then got a hit. You can be certain that the next time he comes up to the plate, he will adjust his cap, tap the plate once, and take two short practice swings. If he gets another hit, he will probably be following this procedure for a very, very long time. And, even if he doesn't get a hit the next time, he is liable to go hitless for thirty or more attempts before he changes this ritual. About the only way the ritual is likely to be changed is if he forgets to do it, and gets another hit anyway.

But, this really doesn't present a counter-example to my argument.

Rather than becoming free of the first ritual, he is almost certain to adopt the "new" ritual. Consequently, a real or imagined success that is assigned to a protocol for real or imagined reasons is a strong factor in the retention of that protocol.

It is not the most important factor, however. If the thoughts and strategies that you have used in the past worked AND you are still breathing, you will use them again because you will assign to these procedures special powers, something that I call Survival Value.

There is somewhere within us the knowledge that, if we do something wrong, we could die. The first thing we check after almost any event is whether or not we are still alive.[58] If we are still alive, then the actions that we carried out during the event are seen as promoting survival. It is often this aspect of our protocols acquiring Survival Value that makes them so difficult to change.

Why would one forsake behaviors which have worked in the past and which have demonstrated Survival Value for any new and untried behavior? We come to the conclusion that those ways of being and doing things that we have used in the past have proven to be of value. The greatest proof we have is that we are

---

[58] As everyday experiences and a sense of personal security become more commonplace these little processes of life verification become so "automatic" that they are rarely acknowledged, but they still occur. For most of us, it requires some special event to make us respond in this way overtly.

still alive. Consequently, any change from our past procedures threatens our sense of what we believe we have done in the past to remain alive. And this is often the root cause behind why we don't want to change.

In class, I constantly kid my students about why the process of change is taking longer than they would like it to. Rather than reminding them of the influence of Survival Value, I say to them, "Why are you so discouraged about how long this is taking? All I'm asking you to do is change everything about yourself." And one of the most important things that we are trying to change is this underlying conviction that there is a causal, immediate, and non-trivial relationship between the way in which we have always done things and the fact that we are still alive.

*   *   *   *   *

During a skiing lesson, one of my first ski instructors was making exactly this point. He told me that what makes skiing so hard to learn is that everything you need to do to ski well and safely is the opposite of the way that it seems it should be.[59]

On your first day of skiing, there you are poised at the top of the terrifyingly steep bunny slope. You are about to tilt forward in a death-defying act. As you start your horrifying descent, your immediate reaction is to lean back on your skis, lean back towards the upper part of the hill, and to turn your body away from the direction in which you are falling down the slope. The person you are with, who is trying to teach you how to ski, then insists that you should bring your weight forward, place it over the downhill ski, and keep your upper body turned facing downhill. This places you in a terrible conflict.

There you are, hurtling down some mountain, and everything you have ever learned or believed is telling you that what you are being asked to do can't be done safely. The decisions, strategies, and commands which have served you well before and which have always kept you alive in the past now threaten to send you over some cliff or, at least, into some snow bank.

My instructor then told me about the most amazing skiing lesson he had ever taught.

A man who appeared to be in his late thirties came in for his first lesson on his first day of skiing. Because the man valued instruction, he had set up a two-

---

[59] Anyone who does not downhill ski and who is still unconvinced about the close relationship of learning new and different activities to a sense of survival is encouraged to start skiing. Anyone who learned to downhill ski as an adult, or at least as someone old enough to have acquired the wisdom of fear before starting, is encouraged to remember their early experiences.

hour lesson. The instructor very carefully explained what his student should do to ski and explained that his instructions would seem all wrong but that they needed to be done anyway. As the two of them started skiing, the new student did everything the instructor asked of him almost as soon as he asked for it and without variation. Consequently, the new student began to progress dramatically.

As the student progressed, the instructor took his beginner on increasingly difficult terrain, first to see if he could handle it, and then to see how far he could go. Even though the lesson took slightly more than the scheduled two hours, by the end of his first lesson, the "beginner" was expertly skiing the most difficult terrain available.

The somewhat astonished instructor then told his student what he had accomplished and asked him if he knew of any reason why he had done so well and learned so quickly. The student laughed and explained.

He said the reason why he had time to be skiing was because he had recently retired from the air force where he had been a test pilot for fighter planes for over twenty years. As such, of course, his coordination and conditioning were very high. More importantly, though, the ex-pilot credited his training for his rapid progress.

At very high speeds, certain maneuvers that he performed in his jet plane produced tremendous amounts of pressure and disorientation. In fact, some maneuvers create such pressure that the pilot will almost certainly "black-out" while performing them. When this happens the disorientation can be almost complete. It is very common upon regaining consciousness for the pilot not to know where the ground is, or worse, have a very strong – but incorrect – conviction about where the ground is.

When this happens, the pilot has been trained to put aside his conviction about the ground's location and go through a particular protocol for reading his instruments. Then, he must ignore his belief about his orientation and make the maneuvers appropriate to what his instruments say even when they are different from his "feelings."

The former pilot said flying his plane according to the panel, and against what he believed, is the scariest thing he had ever learned to do, but it had saved his life many, many times. So, when the ski instructor asked him to ignore his convictions and "throw his body down the hill", he relied on his training and his confidence in the instructor and simply did as he was told. Because he did what he was told, and because he received good instruction, and because he had a high degree of fitness and coordination, he became an expert skier on his very first day.

In a way, though, there is no difference between our new skier, our stair-climbing little girl, and what they both did.

Both had developed behavior response patterns that had served them well. Both had employed these response patterns and were still breathing. Both, therefore, would be likely, when faced with new activities or experiences, to rely upon these old response patterns and the patterns of thoughts and commands that engendered them because they wanted to continue to have success and survive. The only difference between them was the sophistication of their different strategies and the realities of the dangers that they faced.

The little girl's strategy was appropriately childish, based on a child's perception and formulation of the problem. The pilot's procedures were based on training and a process of reasoning nearly as sophisticated as the planes that he flew. Still, both people – at the critical moment of going from planning through "thinking" and, hence, into activity – reverted back to the commands and procedures which they had used before, and which, after having used them "successfully", had kept them alive.

So, the first value we place upon any given response pattern is our perception of its Survival Value. To us, a good response pattern is any pattern that we use with some success, and that after we use it we are still alive. Although these response patterns don't really have the special powers we assign to them, it seems that we respect and hold them sacred as if they did

*   *   *   *   *

Another major determining factor in the persistence of a given response pattern is what I call Virtue Points.

Any strategy that has Survival Value by being associated with a positive result AND which earns praise also earns Virtue Points. The greater the positive outcome and/or the greater the praise, the greater the number of Virtue Points a given strategy will receive. The greater the number of Virtue Points which accrues to any given strategy, the more difficult it becomes to change the strategy or put it aside.[60]

One day in class, I was talking about the fun I was having teaching myself to shoot baskets more efficiently. The class decided that what they wanted to do

---

[60] We can see that in our previous examples both Survival Value and Virtue Points were involved. The little girl achieved the ability to move between levels of her house without being carried as well as praise from her parents for being such a big girl. The batter went on a hitting streak "because" of his ritual. The test pilot lived long enough to learn to ski in a day. It is important to see that Survival Value and Virtue Points are difficult to separate. While, in most cases, it is the Virtue Points that will determine the staying power of a given strategy, it must never be forgotten that often the depth of feeling associated with these decisions to persist in a strategy is as strong as survival itself.

next was to have a lesson in learning how to shoot a basketball. We all went out to the basketball court and worked on the process of learning a new skill.

Most of the class members, by following instructions, began having a certain degree of success that surprised and delighted them. One person, however, continued to miss every shot. Finally, when I tossed him the ball and began saying out loud the commands he should be thinking to increase the probability of his success as I had done before, he very clearly ignored what I was saying, looked down at the ground next to his right foot as he bounced the ball, and then threw the ball towards the basket.

The absolute worst of all possible consequences occurred.

The ball went in the basket!

From that point on, there was nothing that I could say or do which would stop him from looking at the ground near his right foot while bouncing the ball just before he took a shot. He had come to associate successful shooting of a basketball with moving his eyes and head away from the basket just before he let go of the ball.

The fact that he never made another shot when he did this did not dissuade him from the practice. A discussion of what was involved in the process of shooting and the strategies most likely to enhance the probability of making a shot elicited from him complete and total theoretical agreement that looking at the basket while shooting was a requirement of making a good shot. It did not, however, prevent him from looking away the next time he took a shot.

The student had confused the coincidence of making a basket while looking away from the basket with the belief that there was a causal relationship between the two events. There was now within him a conviction, in spite of common sense, that successfully shooting a basketball required looking away just before you released the ball.

When he had first shot the ball at the basket and looked at the basket at the same time, he had had no success at all even though he had followed the instructions as best he could. The one time he looked away out of desperation and frustration before he shot the ball was the only time the ball went in.

The ball went in. He was still alive. His classmates cheered. That settled it! He had become convinced that this procedure of looking down and to the right of his feet – away from the basket – while bouncing the ball just prior to shooting was the way to shoot baskets successfully.

The fact that he never made another basket was not enough reason for him to change the way he shot the ball. The fact that the ball's going into the basket that one time had everything to do with the distance, direction, and pathway in which he threw the ball and had nothing to do with looking away was not enough reason for him to change his "proven" procedure. The fact that there is nearly universal agreement among the experts that the best way to enhance the probability of putting the ball in the basket is by looking at the basket was not enough reason for him to change.

The only facts of importance to him were that he had looked away; he had shot the ball; the ball had gone into the basket; he was alive; and his classmates had cheered. His mind was made up! For him, the best and only way to shoot basketballs was looking away from the basket and down and to the right while bouncing the ball as you get ready to shoot.

From then on, every time the stimulus for shooting a basketball came to his mind, he called forth from his storehouse of directive guidance protocols the commands which were present the one time he enjoyed success. These commands included the commands associated with glancing down and to the right in the sequence of events that precede shooting the ball. Unless he were to make a very determined effort to change these commands – to escape their dominance – they will always remain in place and in charge. As a result, until he disciplines himself to make the changes required, he will always look away before he shoots.[61]

*   *   *   *   *

Armed with these concepts of Survival Value and Virtue Points, it might be advantageous to look again at the behaviors of some people we saw earlier.

Do you remember our marching cadet?

This was the fellow who walked in such a bizarre way because he was trying to avoid stepping on the heels of the cadet marching in front of him – more than thirty years after the cadet in front of him had left. While he was in military school, he had had a number of problems. One of these problems was this problem of hitting the heels of the guy marching in front of him during close order drill. He told me that not only did the guys who were getting their heels clipped give him a hard time, but he was also being constantly harassed by the instructors and the commandant.

I'm sure he was under such pressure to come up with a solution that he never heard the solutions offered to him by his instructors. When he finally came upon this bizarre strategy for walking that allowed him to stop hitting the other cadet's heels, I'll bet he was swimming in Virtue Points (not to mention the "Survival Value" of not being hit by his classmates). In fact, the strength of the Virtue

---

[61] By the way, some years after this event, I asked this same student in a class to pantomime shooting a basketball, and every time I asked him to do it, he still looked down and to the right while "bouncing" the ball before "shooting".

Points was so great that more than thirty years after he had last marched in close order drill he still walked the same way to avoid the heels of the cadet marching in front of him.

Then there was the little girl who was using muscular contraction throughout her body to "keep the world from falling apart".

There is no doubt that she was under a lot of pressure in her parental home. Her perception of her world was that it was falling apart. On one level, the holding together of the world by proxy – by holding her joints together – was a brilliant kind of solution.

Within her home, she was in a relatively powerless position. Within her home, there was little she could do to change her parents, their behavior in general, or their behavior towards one another specifically, including the enduring threat on their part to separate as a couple. She did have some control over her muscles, however. By intentionally keeping her muscles tied together, she could be exerting her will in the kind of omnipotent way that only children ought to believe in, forcing the world to conform to her desires. As long as her parents stayed together, she received Virtue Points for having brought it about. When they finally broke up, she initially consoled herself for having kept her parents together for so long and then she redoubled her efforts to keep the "rest of the world" from falling apart any further.

Both of these people continued to carry out behavior in the present day that was initiated by commands that were created in response to specific problems from very long ago. Both behaviors "worked". From their points of view, these behaviors made sense. From another point of view, however, neither behavior made any sense at all.

When I asked the cadet to show me how he walked before he went to military school, he immediately started walking, but in a very different pattern, one which featured an exaggerated throwing of his feet directly forward. If the cadet had been able to follow the directions of his drill instructors for stopping the distortions in this earlier form of walking, the problem of hitting the other person's heels would not have come up. But, his condition of general coordination was already so bad, and the strength of his habitual patterns of directive guidance so strong by the time he went away to school, he couldn't easily stop his old way of walking and the only solution which "worked" was to exaggerate his pre-existing movement faults still further by forcing his legs higher and into a different direction, one which kept the original distortion but turned his legs away from striking the cadet in front of him.

There are two points to be taken away from my student's ability to re-create immediately his older way of walking.

In the first place, the commands that were required to create this older way of walking were instantly accessible and ready to be used. These particular commands were ready to be used immediately in spite of the long period in which they had not been used. Secondly, the commands that created his later non-heel-kicking walk were based on adjusting the older sets of commands to accomplish directly the immediate goal at hand. Not only were the patterns of directive guidance that he had learned to use in his older way of walking still intact and ready to be used, they were being used as the basis for his newer form of walking. The difference between the two gaits was due to adding in even more unnecessary muscular effort in the second way of walking. This only served to distort further the misshapenness of the preceding walk rather than bringing about a more efficient and effective way of walking.

The little girl's behavior of clamping down on her muscles to keep the world from falling apart makes even less sense, but – from the very first day she tried it – the world didn't fall apart. Every time there was another family crisis, she increased her efforts to meet the needs of the crisis and the world didn't fall apart again. Even on those occasions when events didn't turn out in the way that she wanted, she experienced relief and satisfaction in the knowledge that her efforts had prevented them from turning out worse. This strategy for survival had progressed to the point that, by the time she came into my office for treatment, her sense of "zero muscular effort" involved such a powerful and continuous pulling of her muscles against herself that she was creating premature structural degeneration in herself while living a relatively sedentary life.

Holding tightly onto all of her muscles in order to avoid or resolve family crises is no more likely to be a strategy for success than looking away from the basket in order to shoot a basketball and in many ways it is even less likely to bring about success. In both cases, however, our friends mistakenly assigned the power of a causal relationship to circumstances where no causal relationship exists. Yet, they both had a strong and enduring conviction about the necessity for carrying out their incidental behaviors as a means of achieving their ends.

*   *   *   *   *

This is the trap in which we can all find ourselves. Like all of these people, all of us can be trapped by the dominance of the procedures that we have used before.[62]

In the first place, as Alexander pointed out, the movements that we make create feelings. Over time, the feelings that are created by the movements that we make and the way that we make them come to feel familiar. It is this increasing

---

[62] A much more thorough discussion of these last points can be found in Volume II of *The Alexander Commentaries* in the section on the Three Universal Delusions.

sense of familiarity – not the appropriateness of the movement – that causes the way we have always moved to "feel right." Alexander believed it was the desire to move in a way that produces this familiar feeling that leads to repeating previous movement strategies. "The lure of the familiar proves too strong for [us] and keeps [us] tied down to the habitual use of [ourselves] which *feels right*."[63] In other words, "*the desire to feel right in the gaining of (our ends becomes our)* primary desire."[64]

Secondly, we have performed certain acts and enjoyed certain successes and drawn certain, usually unexamined, conclusions about the causal interrelationships of the way we do things to the success we enjoy. As long as we remain alive, we will always have the sense that the way we have performed our activities promoted survival. This, in itself, is enough incentive to continue with our activities as we have always done them.

In addition to these incentives, we have Virtue Points heaped upon us as we grow up. The acceptance of these Virtue Points creates in our minds an even closer connection between how we have done things and receiving what we want. Even in those cases in which there is no actual, causal relationship between the little "rituals" we perform and the success that we enjoy, we have come to believe that there is.

What is more, we delude ourselves about being in control of these relationships and ourselves. We believe that the outcome of the events that have occurred was based on our intention, rather than merely being caused by the actions performed while carrying out our habitual patterns of thought and analysis. In my parental home we acknowledged this "truth" by saying, "If it happened that way, it's because we planned it that way."

Our problem is that through the course of growing up, we have adopted certain strategies and behaviors that we keep active and in place and then fit them as best we can to our perceived needs at any given time. These strategies and behaviors have often come about in a haphazard way without regard for planning or efficiency. In those cases where this kind of training has proven sufficient for us to become the kind of people we want to be, to achieve the goals we have set for our lives, and to reach all of our dreams, there is no need for any other form of organizing our thoughts. This kind of haphazard, happy outcome, however, is usually the exception and not the rule.

The problem is that, all too often, we, like the basketball player, mistake the fact of a success for the belief that the success we enjoyed was caused by what we believed we had done in the way we had done it. We have the belief that the success of our ventures is always due to the planning and execution of our

---

[63]   Alexander, F, M,. *The Use of the Self*. Gollancz, London, 1985, p. 59.
[64]   *ibid.*, p. 59.

imagined response design. As long as things are going well, this mistaken evaluation remains harmless. It is when things do not go well that problems occur.

If we believe that what we do and how we think we do it is the genuine cause of our success when it is not the genuine cause, we create a problem for ourselves when faced with failure. In such cases, we often believe that our only course of action is to increase the amount of effort used to do the things we did before in order to create future success. This is what the little girl did by tightening her muscles even more.

Even when we are given appropriate "corrections" from the outside, as our marching cadet was, the probability of genuine success and change remains slight because the corrections will be carried out within the context of the faulty habitual commands already in place. We will continue to work on the corrections using our faulty habitual commands until our experience satisfies our distorted conceptions of movement and self, or until we believe the person correcting us is satisfied.

There is no question that our cadet was satisfied and pleased by his final movement solutions for the problem of walking. He was even proud. So proud in fact, that he continued this brand of walking as a kind of kinetic badge of courage long after the need for the solution had graduated and disappeared.

And what if an individual who desires to change decides to listen to the appropriate corrections he has been given? What if this individual has decided that he will stay with the "thinking" required to create the appropriate commands to bring about the changed behavior that he desires? What if he has decided not to be concerned about whether or not this new behavior feels right, and is only concerned that he is carrying out his new commands for movement?

He will find, as Alexander did initially, that his "mind" (at least in its current state of discipline) is not the superior directive agent. He will find that his reliance upon his past patterns of directive guidance is practically irresistible. He will find that these patterns of directive guidance dominate all of his activities and the manner in which they are performed. He will find that these concepts of guidance were formed without much regard for cause and effect, but rather had more to do with familiarity and survival and praise. He will find that he is unable to change because, rather than having trained his mind to guide his actions, the commands associated with his prior actions have come to "train" his mind. He will find that he has come to believe that his mind is still in charge when, in fact, it is the habitual patterns of thought "inmates" who are running the directive guidance "asylum". He will find that his problem is that he is unable to change his responses to stimuli because the commands associated with his previous responses are not the servant to his intentions and desires, but have become the masters of his responses.

If we are ever to change successfully, we must learn to train our minds to dominate our previous protocols of directive guidance. We must train our minds to operate on principles of directive guidance that are conscious, reasoned, flexible, and themselves subject to evaluation and change. We must train our minds to the point that we can continuously overcome the dominance of these habitual patterns of directive guidance and escape their habitual tyranny.

This is precisely what Alexander did and what he encourages us to do.

For those of us who are satisfied with the results that we have achieved through the continuous employment of our habitual patterns of directive guidance, there is no need to go through the training required to create the mental disciplines that will reorganize our thoughts in a more constructive way. But, for those of us who believe that we can become a little bit better, happier, and more fulfilled, for those of us who want more and who are willing to pay the cost of becoming more than we already are, these instinctive, subconscious, and unreasoned patterns of directive guidance which are responsible for initiating our usual responses are not good enough. We must learn to find ways to bring these patterns of guidance up to a level of reasoning and understanding where we can hope to make a change, and free ourselves of the dominance of these old habitual patterns of thought.

The only way we will ever effectively change the manner of our response to stimuli is to discover a way to challenge the dominance of these habitual patterns of directive guidance. We must re-evaluate all of our pet strategies and ways of doing things, no matter how much Survival Value they have for us or how many Virtue Points they may have accrued, or even how familiar those ways of doing things have come to feel. We must put aside our reliance upon correction as a restorative procedure, and learn to trust in something other than our feelings as a guide for our movement behavior. We must learn to identify and overcome our incorrect conceptions and fixed ideas, and substitute for them a clear understanding of the ways in which we are made and the ways in which we work. We must carry out the same procedures that Alexander did when he was faced with the experience of continuing failure and we must acquire the same mental disciplines that allowed him to achieve all of his success.

In other words, we must find a way to probate man's supreme inheritance – the power of the conscious mind to acquire complete control of all our potentialities – or we will be left forever in the muddle that Alexander described.

THE MENTAL DISCIPLINES

Chapter 11

THE THREE PART PROCESS
OF PROTOCOL DESIGN

IN THE FIRST CHAPTER of his third book, *The Use of the Self,* Alexander describes the experiences and decisions he went through in gaining his ability to change the use of himself in activity. I believe that this chapter is the most important document in all of the literature that pertains to the Alexander Technique. It is in this chapter that Alexander provides a blueprint for change. Here, an answer can be found in black and white to all of the questions about what Alexander did to improve himself. It is in this chapter that Alexander sets out clearly and in their proper sequence all of the stages that he went through in the development of his work.

In the next section, we will look at the five mental disciplines that Alexander describes. While the discussion will necessarily be briefer than it deserves, I believe that, through the study and practice of these disciplines, the reader will come into possession of all the tools required to learn how to do Alexander's work. Through the understanding that comes from the practice of these disciplines, I believe that anyone can learn how to overcome the problems caused by his or her own habitual patterns of directive guidance and to achieve a satisfactory source of direction for the use of himself in activity. In time, the student will come to own the ideas that make up Alexander's work and the mental disciplines that make up his technique for change.[65] Once this condition has been reached, then the seemingly limitless power for constant self-improvement that is the primary benefit of this work will be the student's forever.

Before we begin, however, I think it would be important to talk about an aspect of Alexander's chapter that is the source of much confusion in understanding both Alexander's process and his work.

*   *   *   *   *

---

[65] In the Basic Principles class, the concept of "Owning an Idea" means knowing something so well that your understanding of the idea and your ability to convey the information to someone else is independent of circumstances. If you own an idea, there is nothing anyone can say or do which will confuse you about it. If you own an idea, you can explain and demonstrate it easily in a variety of ways. An owned idea is one which has a practical basis and one in which you have complete understanding and confidence. It is more than the ability to recite words at will. It is the certainty about your experience of the ideas involved which allows you to articulate the concept in your own way – or many other ways – in any situation.

Alexander wrote this chapter as though it were written in a kind of past-present tense. Although he is writing about events that had occurred forty years in the past, he writes about each stage of understanding with the command of only the knowledge that he had at each stage. He does this by making each point of understanding as real and as limited as once it was. In other words, instead of writing an essay, he tells us a story. Perhaps it was his sensitivity as an actor that led him to show us what happened as it happened rather than tell us everything about it afterwards, but I think he had a much more important reason for presenting this material in this way.

Like an actor in a play, Alexander shares each discovery in his adventure, each belief, as it occurred to him and as he believed it to be true at that time. He tells us this information in this way to make us go through the same steps that he did in the way that he did it. This authenticity to the truth of each moment and step, even when it does not speak well of him, is what I mean when I say that in this chapter Alexander displays an incredible and illuminating style of narrative integrity. Writing this chapter in this way not only gives us an insight into the process of reasoning and experimentation he used in creating his technique, but by presenting it in story form, he elevates our experience of this process to the level of a teaching myth. While the use of this conceit creates a teaching document of unsurpassed power, it has also served as a source of confusion to those students who did not understand the author's style or the intent behind it.

Most books like Alexander's are written in a straightforward essay style. In fact, except for this chapter, all the rest of Alexander's writing is in this kind of essay form. When working with an essay, it is a common and appropriate practice for the reader to extract bits and pieces of the author's argument, and to represent these pieces as some significant portion of the argument as a whole. In fact, Alexander tells us that we can't avoid being drawn to those particular bits and pieces that conform to our preconceived values and ideas just as we can't avoid rejecting passages with which we are in disagreement.[66] Because of our preference for passages that confirm our present prejudices, any kind of dogmatic use of aphorisms in teaching is a risky proposition. It is much easier still to commit this kind of error in this particular chapter because the author is not writing with the omniscience of the essayist or even with the conviction and

---

[66]   Support for this claim can be found in the chapter from *Constructive Conscious Control of the Individual* entitled, "Incorrect Conception," e.g., "The great fact that must be realized (is that) we all think and act ... in accordance with the peculiarities of our particular psycho-physical make-up." (STAT edition, page 108) and in the chapter entitled "Habits of Thought and of Body" from *Man's Supreme Inheritance,* e.g., "The disputants (in an argument) have so influenced their own minds that ... (the) part of their intelligence normally susceptible of receiving new ideas ... is in a state of amnesia; it is shut off, put out of action." (Mouritz edition, page 46) In fact, this is a recurring theme that can be found throughout all of Alexander's books.

guidance of his final conclusions, but with the peculiar momentary blindness of an individual presently caught up in a given set of events.

To understand what Alexander is trying to say in this chapter, one must not only understand each part of the story as it happens, but must also understand how the parts relate to one another and how subsequent events either confirm or deny earlier impressions and conclusions. Sometimes a "truth" that is proclaimed loudly on one page will be emphatically denied by the events and conclusions that follow. This is precisely the process and skill that an actor uses in studying and performing a part. There must be a commitment to the "truths" of the moment in any given scene, but the way any particular moment fits in with the integrity of the play as a whole must never be lost.

When reading Alexander's narrative, therefore, I believe that it is important for the reader to apply this same kind of overview process, this peculiar skill of the actor – to see how the "truths" of the section being read relate to other "truths" in other sections and the whole piece simultaneously. It is only by understanding the function of each part of the story in the context of the whole that any actual truth value can be assigned to the statements and claims that are made. This is important because I believe that Alexander's background as an actor led him to write with the assumption that the reader would employ this manner of study in his reading, and that the fact that this is the only part of his books to be written in this kind of story-telling, narrative style would be enough of a clue from him for us to treat the specifics of this material differently. He doesn't leave us a direct statement that this approach to the material in this chapter is the correct one, but I think this is because he thought the use of this kind of narrative style was an explicit enough clue already that we were to do so.

Because of all of this, I advise my students to beware the temptation to pick out any small piece of what Alexander has written and to brandish it as any kind of "answer" without relating it to a larger context or the whole of what Alexander wrote. This warning is valid in all of Alexander's writings, but nowhere as much as in this chapter. The need for this kind of comprehensive approach to the study of Alexander's writings in general and the need for developing the tools necessary to accomplish this type of study provided the fuel for the creation of both my Basic Principles course and the writing of *The Alexander Commentaries*. The whole of the second volume of this series is devoted to this first chapter in Alexander's third book and provides an investigation of Alexander's description of his experiences in much greater detail than is appropriate here.

*   *   *   *   *

In the first half of "The Evolution of a Technique," Alexander concerns himself with what we might call the more physical aspects of his use.

In this part of the chapter, he discovers his harmful tendencies in speech. He associates these tendencies with the shortening of his stature. He learns that while he cannot exert a direct control over all of these tendencies, he can exert an indirect one. He learns the importance of moving his head not just forward, but forward and up. He discovers the close connection between use and functioning. He finds out that the misuse of his vocal mechanism is associated with a misuse of his other parts in the actions attendant to the process of speaking. Finally, it gradually dawns upon him that these individual wrong uses actually constitute a habitual wrong use of his mechanism as a whole.

Further, he recognizes that the strength of this harmful manner of response was not only due to the fact that it was habitual, but that he had cultivated it as well. In addition, he discovered that it was the influence of this use and not the use itself that caused his problems.

The influence of this *cultivated* habitual use, therefore, acted as an almost irresistible stimulus to me to use myself in the wrong way I was accustomed to; this stimulus to general wrong use was far stronger than the stimulus of my desire to employ the new use of my head and neck, and I now saw that it was this influence which led me, as soon as I stood up to recite, to put my head in the opposite direction to that which I desired.[67]

All of Alexander's discoveries to this point were important and helpful. The succeeding discoveries could not have occurred without them. But, at this point, when Alexander discovered the importance of this practically irresistible influence upon the manner of his response to stimuli, he reached the most important turning point in his investigation.

It was at this point that his investigation turned from the discovery of appropriate physical corrections for a faulty mechanical event to an investigation of the means by which all mechanical events are directed. He turned from looking at how the different parts of our physical mechanism interact (a subject which he knew a great deal about) to the search for the source of guidance for all events. It was at this point that Alexander wrote what I take to be the most important sentence in all of his work.

For, it is at this point, the point at which Alexander understood how to deal with his problems on the physical plane as well as the importance and power of his cultivated habits – after he had understood the mechanical imperatives involved in the interaction of his body parts in movement; after he had understood the importance of "forward and up", "lengthening the stature" and so forth; after he had already enjoyed a gratifying degree of success in overcoming his original problem – it is after all of this that he writes, "I now had proof of one thing at

---

[67]   Alexander, F.M., *The Use of the Self*. Gollancz, London, 1985, p. 34.

least, that all of my efforts up till now to improve the use of myself in reciting had been misdirected."[68, 69]

Alexander now believed that his efforts had been misdirected because he had discovered that the key to improving the use of one's self in activity was not in finding any mechanically based solution to his problem or in employing any rote and repetitive process of directing himself, but in learning how to operate the means of directive guidance that created his responses. All of Alexander's previous efforts with physical-result-oriented procedures gave him the tools and skills with which to proceed, but it was this investigation of the means of controlling the patterns of directive guidance – not just altering his physical responses – which he recognized as being of the utmost importance. It was the process of raising this source of mental control from the instinctive onto the conscious, reasoning plane that now formed the central focus of Alexander's story and work.

*   *   *   *   *

As we talked about before, Alexander's first efforts to change how he directed himself in activity began with an investigation of how "feelings" were used for guidance. In fact, when he began to look for a source of directive guidance, being guided by "feelings" seemed to provide the only answer that he could initially find. As he looked further, however, he found that there was a discrepancy between what he thought he was doing and what he actually did. As he watched others, he found this same sort of discrepancy. (The only difference was one of degree.) In fact, he discovered that our "instinctive control and direction of use had become so unsatisfactory, and the associated feeling so untrustworthy as a guide, that it could lead us to do the very opposite of what we wished or thought we were doing."[70]

It was at this point that he started his search for a means to restore trustworthiness of feeling as a guide. In this search, however, three points in particular impressed him.

---

[68]   _ibid._, p. 34.

[69]   I always feel it is important at this point in my classes to go over the difference between "misdirected" and "wasted." Alexander does not suggest that all of his efforts and insights and training prior to this time were wasted. In fact, he makes it very clear that he benefited greatly from all of those experiences. There is no question that he also benefited from the kinds of constructive changes in postural and movement behavior that he describes earlier in the chapter. These kinds of beneficial changes happen daily and may very well satisfy the student in search of relief or improved performance. If, however, the goal of the student or the teacher is to improve the use of him- or herself in activities as a general discipline and principle, then efforts focused on the more physical aspects of the training will be efforts, like Alexander's, which will have been misdirected.

[70]   _ibid._, p. 38.

Firstly, by observing that when he did not move his head as he intended, he had proof that his actions were being misdirected and that the misdirection was associated with his untrustworthy feelings. Secondly, this misdirection was in place and functioning seemingly on its own and, together with the untrustworthy feelings associated with it, made up his habitual use of himself. Thirdly, this instinctive misdirection which was associated with the wrong use of his head and neck and which led to the wrong habitual use of himself was initiated by the decision to use his voice. In other words, this misdirection was his instinctive reaction to the stimulus to use his voice.

When he thought about that last point, he decided that if the misdirection came as a reaction to the decision to use his voice, and if he could find a way to stop his misdirection which started with the wrong habitual use of his head and neck, he would be stopping his whole unsatisfactory reaction at its source. Once his initial, misdirected reaction was stopped, he could then look for a direction of himself that would guarantee an improved use of his head and neck. He believed that the manner of guiding himself in activity associated with a new and improved use of his head and neck would provide a satisfactory use of himself in reaction to the stimulus to speak.[71]

As with all of Alexander's decisions, conclusions, and discoveries, these ideas led to a period of practical investigation. As Frank Jones points out, there is no "mere theorizing" in Alexander's work. All of Alexander's theories "were derived from his own experience in establishing a degree of conscious control over his own stereotyped behavior."[72] Every conclusion that Alexander reached and espoused was the result of empirical investigation.

The experiments which Alexander performed as a result of his new reasoning led to two major conclusions: the first dealt with the appropriateness of feeling as a guide and the second set out a plan for creating appropriate responses to stimuli.

*   *   *   *   *

Alexander begins this next section of his chapter by writing, "In the work that followed I came to see that to get a direction of my use which would ensure [a] satisfactory reaction, I must cease to rely upon the feeling associated with my instinctive direction and in its place ...".[73]

Now if Alexander had still been interested in the process of making feelings more trustworthy again for the purpose of directive guidance, he would have probably finished this sentence with something like: "I must cease to rely upon

---

[71] These last two paragraphs follow Alexander's text very closely. *ibid.*, pp. 38-9.

[72] Jones, Frank Pierce, *Freedom to Change*. Mouritz, London, 1997, p. 28.

[73] Alexander, F.M., *The Use of the Self*. Gollancz, London, 1986, p. 39.

the feeling associated with my instinctive direction and in its place employ the feeling associated with my newly retrained and trustworthy sense of direction." But, this isn't what he writes at all. What Alexander actually writes is "that to get a direction of my use which would ensure [a] satisfactory reaction, I must cease to rely upon the feeling associated with my instinctive direction, and in its place employ my reasoning processes."[74]

Continuing in this same sentence, he outlines a particular three-part process for designing protocols of response to stimuli. It is this switch from his previous use of instinctive processes of guidance by "feeling" to a means of guidance that is directed by his reasoning processes and is not associated with feeling at all which provides the first cornerstone of the foundation for the process of change that is his work.

"In short," Alexander wrote, "I concluded that if I were ever able to react satisfactorily to the stimulus to use my voice, I must replace my old, instinctive (unreasoned) direction of myself by a new, conscious (reasoned) direction."[75] He decided he must replace the old manner of directing himself that was associated with feelings – of all degrees of trustworthiness – and replace it with a manner of directing himself that was based on his reason and reasoning. Any directive guidance based on his reason and reasoning would necessarily be divorced from his feelings in any direct or causal way.

*   *   *   *   *

Alexander decided that if he was ever to get a direction of his use that would ensure a satisfactory reaction, he must employ his reasoning processes:

1. to analyze the conditions of use present;

2. to select (reason out) the means whereby a more satisfactory use could be brought about;

3. to project consciously the directions required for putting these means into effect.[76]

In my classes, we generalize these three rules and call this the Three Part Process for Protocol Design.[77]

---

[74] *ibid.*, p. 39. This is the first time that Alexander suggests an alternative for his earlier concept of guidance by feeling. For the first time he decides that he will set aside guidance by feeling and replace it with a new source of direction that relies on his reasoning processes instead.

[75] *ibid.*, p. 39. In this sentence, the material in the parentheses, "unreasoned" and "reasoned", are the words that Alexander himself uses as substitutes for "instinctive" and "conscious" and are not authorial interjection.

[76] *ibid.*, p. 39.

In other words, if I am going to perform any activity, I must create a protocol for carrying out that activity. One of the sources I can always call upon are the old protocols I have stored within me. The trouble with this, of course, is by responding with past protocols I am more likely than not going to be distancing myself from where I presently am and what is actually going on now. If I respond with past protocols, at least some part of me will be responding to what went on before: the "conditions past" rather than the "conditions present".

By employing the Three Part Process for Protocol Design, I am placing myself squarely in the present. I am looking at the conditions that are present now and not at what the present conditions remind me of. Because I am looking at the conditions that are present, I can create a response that is tailor-made to the actual situation. I can reason out what procedure or procedures are appropriate to the given situation and then carry out those procedures.

Whenever I think of the freshness of experience implied by this process of analysis and selection, I am reminded of my experiences sweeping leaves off the front porch at Marjorie Barstow's house. This was a task that seemed to happen quite a lot. Although the tedium of doing the job was often offset by having another chance to be with Marjorie, I've got to tell you, she used to drive me nuts when we did it.

Every time Marj would sweep the porch, she would try to figure out the best way to do it. The broom held to the left. The broom held to the right. Left-hand low on the broom. Right hand low on the broom. One hand at the top of the broom. Both hands along the sides. Holding the top hand still and "sweeping" the lower hand (and broom) underneath. Holding the lower hand still and leveraging the leaves forward from the top. Dragging everything forward in a single motion. Sweeping everything along next to yourself while stepping forward. Pushing the leaves in front of you from behind. Sweeping in a circle. Sweeping in a straight line. Sometimes she would actually try all of these things. Sometimes she would just talk about them. But always she would think about the best way of doing the task. I was amazed at how inventive she could be to come up with so many different variations.

Me? I just "swept" the porch. By the time we had finished, though, she would tell me what she had "discovered" about the best way to sweep a porch. The first time we did this together it was interesting.

But, you know what? Every time we swept the leaves off the porch, she did the same damn thing! It nearly drove me crazy!

Usually I would just want to shut off my mind and rush through the chore and run off to something else more interesting. For Marjorie, though, there was

---

[77] The generalized statement of this process would be 1) analyze the conditions present, 2) select the appropriate means you have reasoned out whereby you can gain your end, and 3) project consciously the directions required for putting these means into effect.

nothing more interesting than whatever she was doing at any particular time. She gave it her full attention. She treated it to the full power of her observation and analysis each and every time. And no matter how often she came up with the same answer to the best way to sweep the porch (to me, each "best" solution she created each time we did this looked remarkably like the "best" solutions she had created on previous days), she always went through this same process at the same level of involvement; and her part of the swept porch always looked better (and bigger) than mine.

But it used to bug me that she did it that way. Sometimes I just wanted to shake her and say, "Look! We did this yesterday! Why not just use the way you did it yesterday? It worked pretty well then. It will work just as well now. Cut out all of this exploration crap and get on with it!" But I never said it. And now, a few decades later, I begin to appreciate the importance of this process of staying with the conditions present and actively using your reasoning power to look for the best way to do something.

This process of analyzing the conditions present in order to reason out the most appropriate means whereby an end can be gained is at the heart of Alexander's work.[78] Creating a protocol that is appropriate to the task at hand each and every time is more than simple common sense; it is a hallmark of Alexander's technique. More importantly, it makes good use of another of Alexander's principles: the direct relationship of appropriate protocols to the probability of success.

*   *   *   *   *

In our efforts to succeed, we are so accustomed to keeping our attention on the goal we wish to gain that we lose sight of this important relationship. We misdirect our attention by thinking of the product or goal we wish to achieve rather than the process that we would use to achieve it. By placing our attention on the process of reasoning out and applying appropriate protocols, we enhance the probability of our success because the more appropriate the protocol is to the realization of a given end, the more likely the end will be reached. In fact, if the end is attainable and the protocol being used is appropriate to the attainment of that end, then, by continuing with the carrying out of the protocol, achieving one's goal is inevitable.

Conversely, if the process we have chosen to pursue is inappropriate to the attainment of our goal, the probability of our enjoying success approaches zero. It's not precisely zero because just as it is possible to select an inappropriate

---

[78] In fact Alexander tells us that, "the one great principle on which … man's satisfactory progress in civilization depends (is) the principle of *thinking out the reasonable means whereby a certain end can be achieved"*. (Alexander, F. Matthias, *Constructive Conscious Control of the Individual*. STAT Books, 1997, p. 63.)

process, it's also possible that one might make just the right number of mistakes in just the right sequence to enjoy success in spite of what one thinks one is doing. As a friend of mine who has caught the flavor of this kind of success of errors is fond of saying, "Even a blind squirrel finds a nut now and then."

Do you remember our friend, the basketball shooter?

There is no way in the world that not looking at the basket before shooting is a success-enhancing strategy. Yet, as chance – or the capricious gods – would have it, the first time he looked away before he shot, everything else went right and the ball went in.

The danger of relying on the repetition of procedures you believe you used in the past, rather than on a reasoned analysis of the conditions present and their relationship to an appropriate protocol, is that the actual cause of one's success might never be found. If, on the other hand, one is constantly disciplining one-self to carry out the analysis of the conditions present and the evaluation of the appropriateness of the means selected to gain one's end, then one will experience a constantly improving sense of causal relationships and an increasing ability to select appropriate means.

The whole key to this Three Part Process for Protocol Design, and the first step to the retraining of one's mind in this work, is learning how to direct one's attention away from focusing on the goal one wishes to achieve in activity as well as the feelings we may have had in the past. This will free us to focus our attention on the recognition, formulation, and execution of the steps that are required in order for us to achieve our goals.

Remember, if the end you wish to gain is achievable and the process you are employing to achieve that goal is appropriate, then, if you continue to carry out the protocol you have reasoned out as being best suited for your purpose, achieving your goal will be inevitable.

Chapter 12

WITHOUT ATTEMPTING TO DO THEM

WITH THE INTRODUCTION of the Three Part Process of Protocol Design, Alexander had now created a way to make an appropriate protocol for every act he would ever perform. He figured that he had now found the answer to all of his problems. He thought that all he had to do was carry out this design process as he performed each and every act. He was confident that he "should be guided by [his] reasoning rather than by [his] feeling when it came to putting this (strategy) into action, and that [his] 'mind' (in its present condition) was the superior and more effective directing agent."[79]

When he began to experiment to prove this hypothesis, however, he discovered a remarkable thing. He found that he could think about these new procedures to improve the use of himself in speaking and enjoy success in changing his new, improved condition only as long as he didn't try to speak. "At the critical moment when [he] attempted to gain [his] end by means which were contrary to those associated with [his] old habits of use, [his] instinctive direction dominated [his] reasoning direction."[80]

In other words, when he began to make a response to the stimulus to speak, he found that in spite of his new decisions and efforts his old habitual patterns of directive guidance were still in place, still sending out commands to his motor mechanism, and still dominating the relatively weaker influence of his newly reasoned out protocols of response. "This meant that the old instinctive direction which, associated with untrustworthy feeling, had been the controlling factor up to that moment in the building up of [his] wrong habitual use, still controlled the *manner* of [his] response, with the inevitable result that [his] old wrong habitual use was again brought into play."[81]

Alexander discovered that as soon as he received the stimulus to speak, he tried to "do" something to speak. When he tried to "do" something to speak, he employed his habitual patterns of directive guidance to "do" it. As soon as these commands went out, he responded by moving in his old habitual manner because the commands that were sent out most quickly and strongly were the commands that created his old habitual patterns of movement. In order to overcome this difficulty, Alexander decided, "If I was ever to be able to change my habitual use and dominate my instinctive direction, *it would be necessary for me*

---

[79] Alexander, F.M., *The Use of the Self*. Gollancz, London, 1985, p. 39.

[80] *ibid.*, p. 40.

[81] *ibid.*, p. 41.

to make the experience of receiving the stimulus to speak and of refusing to do anything immediately in response. "[82]

In other words, his problem began when he received a stimulus to perform an activity, i.e., when he made the decision to do it. As soon as this happened, he tried to do the activity immediately. As soon as he tried to do the activity immediately, even when his activity was to change his manner of use, he called forth the directive guidance commands that brought about his old movement responses.

If he was ever to succeed in making changes in the way he directed himself in activity, he had to find a way to stop this chain of events. He had to find a way to "drive a wedge between stimulus and response".[83] As long as he responded immediately to the stimulus, his response was guaranteed to be created by his old means of directing himself. If he was ever to succeed in making the changes he desired, he had to find a way to prevent this immediate response.

In order to do this, the response that he had to prevent was not a change in the relationship of his head to his body, but a change in the thinking that created his response. In other words, he had to devise a new procedure by which he could train himself to be able to receive a stimulus without making any response whatsoever so that he could finally free himself from his old manner of misdirection. He called this new mental discipline "inhibition".[84]

*   *   *   *   *

In class, there are two points that I make about inhibition that would be of value for us to pursue at this time.

First of all, as a general practice, I think that we would be wise if we would restrict our use of the technical term "inhibition" to this particular mental process of making the experience of receiving a stimulus and of refusing to do anything immediately in response.

Very often you can hear people talk about "practicing inhibition" by deciding to stand up from a chair and then, instead of standing up, they remain on the chair instead. It is as though they think that by staying on the chair, they are

---

[82]   *ibid.*, p. 40.

[83]   Marjory Barlow used this phrase in a lecture at the 2nd International Congress in Brighton discussing, in part, the technical process of inhibition.

[84]   At one point in time, it was very chic to engage in involved discussions about the relative appropriateness of the use of the term "inhibition" in the work. Those who were opposed to the use of the term worried that it might be confused with the Freudian concept of inhibition, meaning the repression of behavior. Alexander himself answers these concerns completely in his second book, *Constructive Conscious Control of the Individual.* (pages 131-2 in the STAT Books edition).

practicing inhibition or proving that they have inhibited. But staying on the chair, in this case, is not inhibition but another mental process called withholding consent, and there is a difference between the mental discipline of inhibition and the mental discipline of withholding consent.

Inhibition is a technical term that refers to a thought process applied with the intention of preventing an immediate response upon the receipt of a stimulus. To be effective, the process of inhibition must be applied before there is a chance for the old patterns of misdirection to be employed. Therefore, with respect to a given stimulus, it must happen "immediately" – if not sooner – or not at all.

The intent of inhibition is to make a constructive dissociation between the reception of a stimulus – internal or external – and any kind of immediate and therefore automatic response. Without this dissociation of thought and movement, the means of directive guidance employed to carry out an activity would almost certainly be the default misdirection that the individual has always used. Without this dissociation, the decision to stand, for instance, will almost certainly bring about a habitual response. With the dissociation generated by the process of inhibition, the decision to stand will bring about no movement whatsoever.

In other words, if one were to respond immediately to a stimulus as it is received, or as a decision is made, the chances of responding in a way other than one's usual manner of response would be small. For one thing, as Alexander points out, an immediate response would not allow for enough time to project sufficiently the directions for the new use in order to dominate the "default" directions for the old use. More importantly, by successfully coupling together the reception of a stimulus to the refusal to do anything immediately in response, we prevent ourselves from making any response at all. As a result, we have the opportunity to make a different response. If we respond too quickly to a stimulus in the way we have always done, the opportunity for change will have been lost and the game will be over. Therefore, the process of inhibition needs to happen immediately – as soon as the stimulus to perform an activity comes – or sooner.[85] In this way, the practice of inhibition is coupled to the individual's reception of the stimulus. Further, it is important to understand that the fact that one practices inhibition with regard to the reception of a particular stimulus has no bearing whatsoever on whether or not the activity related to that stimulus will be performed.

Once I decide to stand up from a chair, I can practice inhibition by making the experience of receiving the stimulus to get out of the chair (created by the

---

[85] My advanced students have discovered that it is very difficult and tedious to be on the alert continuously for any new stimuli so they have adopted the far simpler strategy of inhibiting all immediate responses to all stimuli all of the time. This way they can be sure that whenever any particular stimuli comes along they will make the experience of receiving a stimulus and refusing to do anything immediately in response.

decision to get out of the chair) and refusing to do anything immediately in response. If I do this, then I have practiced inhibition. After that, it doesn't matter what I do, because inhibition is a mental discipline, not a behavioral response. I will have successfully practiced inhibition not because I stayed on the chair, but because I will have performed the mental discipline required.

In other words, if I am sitting on a chair and decide to stand up, and upon receiving this stimulus I refuse to do anything immediately in response, and stay on the chair, I will have successfully practiced inhibition. If, on the other hand, I am sitting on a chair and decide to stand up, and upon receiving this stimulus I refuse to do anything immediately in response, and then, while continuing to refuse to do anything immediately in response, I project the directions for the new use in an appropriate way and stand up, I will still have successfully practiced inhibition because I will have performed the mental discipline required.

And the same would be true if I had followed all of these procedures for practicing this mental discipline and raised my hand instead.

Whether or not I am successfully practicing inhibition has little or nothing to do with what activities I do or do not perform. It has everything to do with whether or not I carry out the mental discipline of making the coupled experience of receiving a stimulus and refusing to do anything immediately in response.

For these reasons, I instruct my students to restrict their usage of the term "inhibition" to the practice of this mental discipline and to describe the decision not to perform a particular activity as withholding consent.

*   *   *   *   *

The second point I like to make about the practice of inhibition is that because inhibition is a mental skill, there is nothing to "do" to practice it. There is no action, movement, or lack of movement that has anything to do with the process of inhibition. It is a mental discipline by which we can escape the automatic responses of our previous misdirections and gain the time necessary to act on our conscious reasoning direction.

Whenever I think about this "problem" of what to "do" to inhibit, I am reminded of a student I had in my Basic Principles course in Washington, D.C. in 1988. One weekend she came in determined to get an answer to her question. When I called on her, she asked, "What do you have to do to inhibit?" When I told her that you have to make the experience of receiving a stimulus and refusing to do anything immediately in response, she said, "Yes, I know that, but what do you have to do to inhibit?"

After several rounds of her asking the same question and my giving the same answer, it became apparent that repeating my previous answer was not going to satisfy her. Usually when an appropriate answer fails to satisfy a student, you can be pretty sure that the student is asking a different question than the one you are answering.

When I listened to her question again, I realized that she had meant the word "do" literally. She wanted to know what she had to "do" in order "not to do" what she ordinarily "did" in activity.

This is very similar to a kind of thinking that Alexander reports finding in almost all of his students. When asking them to sit quietly and do nothing, he writes that they will "immediately [show] all those signs of strain and fixity of attention that [they show] when [they are] asked to do something ... Point this out to the pupil, and he will answer, nine times out of ten, 'I am trying to do nothing!' He actually believes that he has something *to do* to do nothing."[86] But, trying to find out what to "do" in order "not to do" something else is missing the point.

In inhibition, we are not concerned with the actions one does or does not perform as much as we are concerned with how one thinks while performing them. The point of the Alexander Technique is not to improve yourself by substituting "appropriate" movements performed in a newly acquired habitual manner for "inappropriate" movements performed in an older habitual manner. The point of the Alexander Technique is to learn how to change your thinking to enable yourself to acquire a conscious guidance and control of your potentialities, thereby freeing yourself from the shortfalls of your habitual misdirection.

Further, there is a way in which asking, "What can I do to inhibit?" is like asking, "What can I eat to lose weight?" The initiation of the activity in question is almost always certain to doom the project.

When I finally figured out what she was asking, I gave her an answer that she understood, but didn't believe.

I told her that inhibition is a mental skill. I told her that there is no action, movement, or lack of movement that has anything to do with the process of inhibition. I told her that inhibition is a mental discipline by which we can gain the opportunity to change, and the time necessary to accomplish the thinking required to dominate, our old manner of habitual misdirection. As a result, there is nothing to "do" to inhibit.

And how did I know she didn't believe me?

Because for the next few months, every time we had a seminar, she would ask me a new question. And, every time we examined the new question more closely, it always turned out to be the same question: "What do you have to do to

---

[86] Alexander, F.M., *Constructive Conscious Control of the Individual*. STAT Books, London, 1997, p. 173-4.

inhibit?" As a matter of fact, the next year in a different class she asked me the same question again.

"What do you have to do to inhibit?"

Nothing.

Inhibition is a mental skill, a mental discipline by which we can stop the thinking that creates our usual manner of response in order to gain the time necessary to accomplish the thinking required to dominate our old manner of habitual misdirection.

There is nothing to "do" to inhibit.

*   *   *   *   *

This technical definition of inhibition – making the experience of receiving a stimulus and refusing to do anything immediately in response – led Alexander to yet another long period of practical investigation.

For many people, the prospect of yet another "long period of investigation" is incredibly disappointing. In our increasingly instant, microwaveable society, we seem to be caught up in finding the quickest answer to solving problems: the short cut. I am on record in many places as saying that the exacting, straightforward, complete performance of any given task is almost always the short cut, but my point here is slightly different and probably more important.

Much is said about the amount of work Alexander performed to "discover" this work. It is often suggested that because Alexander did all of this work, succeeding generations of students won't have to. This argument has always had a sort of Christian flavor to it, as if Alexander had figuratively "died" upon the "cross" of his experimentation for us, so that, by learning the truths of his conclusions, we can avoid the arduousness of his task.

While I can see the marketing value of offering a thirty- or forty-five lesson course of study to learn the work instead of presenting it as an on-going process of self-discipline and study which can only be fully acquired through hard work over a period of many, many years, I have often believed that the myth that our tasks in learning this work will be shorter and easier because we have teachers who have already done the work before is extremely misleading.

If we are to "do what [Alexander] did," then we must do what he did.

These long periods of experimentation that Alexander performed yielded not only conclusions and understandings, but also skills that are necessary for the learning of the work. Even as early in his investigation as his failure to notice his harmful tendencies of misuse in his ordinary speaking,[87] Alexander attributed his

---

[87]   Lines 153-156 out of 889 lines total.

failure to the lack of "experience in the kind of observation necessary to enable me to detect anything wrong in the way I used myself when speaking."[88] His skill of observing himself accurately came from the actual practice of observation that his investigation required. He could not develop these skills without practice, and neither can we. Nowhere is this rule of skill acquisition through practice more apparent than in learning those skills required to retrain one's thinking.

From the very first day of class, students want to know if they are "doing the Alexander Technique right." Most teachers jump on the last part of this question and chastise their students about their desire to be right. This criticism has some merit, of course, but teachers might serve their students better by paying more attention to the first part of what they said.

In order to learn this work, we are all going to have to come to grips with our desire to "do" something in order to correct a problem. This desire to "do" was what fueled Alexander's immediate responses to stimuli and caused him to appreciate the need for inhibition. Inhibition is the mental discipline that he used to overcome his desire to do and to reach the next level of his investigation. It is the procedure that we must all use if we are to learn his work. It is the procedure that we must all use constantly if we are to continue to progress.

*   *   *   *   *

Another great privilege I have enjoyed in this work was the opportunity in the middle nineties to complete a full course of lessons with Margaret Goldie. Miss Goldie was one of Alexander's first apprentices. She was trained as a teacher prior to the first teacher-training course and she faithfully worked with Alexander for many years. Miss Goldie was dedicated, disciplined, and spoke in a forthright manner that some found daunting. Although she was always proper and polite, she did not hesitate to point out practices in the work with which she did not agree.

A case in point was her attitude towards a relatively new approach to teaching the concept of inhibition that had begun to appear in more conventional approaches to teaching Alexander's work. Some teachers of Miss Goldie's acquaintance had begun to describe the practice of inhibition as a pause between stimulus and action. Although I remain unsure if she meant to make a reference to Coca-Cola, she often rather disdainfully referred to this practice as "the pause that refreshes." She said to me it was as though these people believed that if they placed a momentary pause in the sequence of their activities and then carried on using their old habits of misdirection that they were practicing inhibition. She said that this not only gave them a peculiar hesitating quality to their movements

---

[88] Alexander, F.M., *The Use of the Self.* Gollancz, London, 1985, p. 26.

and responses, but "it demonstrates that they don't understand inhibition at all."[89]

What I believe she meant by this was that this approach to inhibition was treating it like a box to tick off on a checklist rather than an on-going mental discipline. Alexander discovered that one of his greatest obstacles in changing the use of himself in activity – even after he had begun using the Three Part Process of Protocol Design and had begun to make the experience of receiving a stimulus and refusing to do anything immediately in response – was that "the old instinctive direction which ... had been the controlling factor ... in the building up of [his] wrong habitual use, still controlled the *manner* of [his] response, with the inevitable result that [his] old wrong use was again and again brought into play."[90] This was because when he reacted too quickly to his decision to go into activity, he used his old instinctive misdirection to implement his newly reasoned out protocols. In trying to set up an experiment to ensure that he would be able to approach an activity while continuing to inhibit his immediate response (and thereby defeat the dominance of his old misdirection), he came upon a third and very important mental discipline as well.

Alexander tells us that he "decided to confine [his] work to giving [himself] directions for the new 'means-whereby,' instead of actually trying to do them or (even) to relate them to the 'end' of speaking."[91] Alexander explains in a footnote that, by the term "means-whereby," he is referring to the "reasoned means to the gaining of an end" which includes both the "inhibition of [his] habitual use" and "the conscious projection of the new directions necessary to the performance of the different acts involved."[92] This meant that during this next stage of his own development, he not only practiced inhibition while giving himself the directions necessary for carrying out his desired activity but he also deliber-

---

[89] The reference here to the concept of inhibition as the "pause that refreshes" and her low opinion of some teachers' conception of inhibition comes from my personal notes taken following lessons with Miss Goldie circa 1994. Her whole point has been strengthened by an image put forth by John Hunter in his excellent 2002 Memorial Lecture. He refers to an emphasis in teaching made by Erika Whittaker in her teaching of inhibition. (Erika was a member of the first teacher-training course as well as a member of the "other" group of teachers identified by Walter Carrington, i.e., Erika, Marjorie Barstow, and Sir George Trevelyan.) John tells us in the lecture that, "what Erika would emphasize about inhibition is that a stop is not a pause; they are quite different. A pause implies that one is going to do the thing, but not yet. A stop has no such implication ... If you press the pause button on a cassette player, the motor is still engaged; as soon as you release the button the machine can only continue in the same direction it was going. If you press the stop button, other options become available." I am not sure whether John or Erika was responsible for the cassette player image, but I am sure that I am grateful for having made the acquaintance of both this distinction and this image.

[90] Alexander, F.M., *The Use of the Self*. Gollancz, London, 1985, p. 41.

[91] *ibid.,* p. 41.

[92] *ibid.,* p. 41.

ately chose not to put these directions into practice. In other words, he gave himself the directions for going into activity "without attempting to 'do' them".[93] The importance of carrying out this procedure is demonstrated by the amount of time that Alexander did it himself.

He told us that, in his work periods, he would give these directions for "long periods together, for successive days and weeks and sometimes even months without attempting to 'do' them."[94] If we are to gain the same abilities and skills as Alexander, then we will have to invest in the same kinds of practice that he did. The way that most of my students apply these procedures is with a process we call Dr. Connie's How-To Chart.

*   *   *   *   *

After being a student for some time, Dr Amundson told us once in class that she was frustrated because although she didn't believe she knew "how to think", she still felt guilty because she didn't "think" all of the time. To solve this problem, she told us she had devised a little procedure to put into practice every morning. She decided that when she got up in the mornings, she would continue with her usual activities, but for just five minutes every day she would project her directions without attempting to "do" them.

Sometimes she would simply lie in bed and project her directions. Sometimes she would exercise. Sometimes she would put in a load of laundry. The nature of her activity wasn't important. What was important was that she made a deal with herself that, whatever she did, for at least a short period of time, every day, she would give herself directions without attempting to "do" them. She figured that if F.M. could do this for months at a time, she could manage five minutes a day. Further, if she did it in the mornings, her obligation would be satisfied early and she wouldn't have to feel guilty if she didn't "think" for the rest of the day.

When she started this experiment, she did have trouble projecting her orders for five whole minutes at a time. She would become distracted or bored or just plain tired of "thinking" in this way. As the days and weeks passed while she continued her practice every morning, however, she noticed that she had developed another problem: she couldn't stop thinking this way after just five minutes.

As time passed, she noticed she was getting more and more done when she first got up. The quality of her work was improving. And, every time she looked at the clock to see how much of the required five minutes was left, she found that she had already exceeded them – often by large amounts of time. More to

---

[93] *ibid.*, p. 41.

[94] *ibid.*, p. 41.

the point, she found it harder and harder not to "think" in this way at other times as well.

Although I can practice giving my directions without attempting to do them when I am sitting or lying quietly, my favorite place to perform this discipline is when I am using a rowing machine.

I know that I am going to be there for a given period of time. Because of the repetitive nature of the machine, I can be reasonably assured that no major crises of decision are going to occur. I simply practice giving my directions without attempting to "do" them as I continue to row away.

As a result of these practice times, and all the other times I project these orders without attempting to "do" them, the nature of my thinking processes has radically changed. The window of opportunity initiated by the process of inhibition has been enlarged by the skills learned in this new procedure. Now I can not only receive a stimulus from the environment and refuse to do anything immediately in response, but I can actually tell myself directly to do something and still prevent an immediate response.

This process of projecting directions without attempting to "do" them is not the "Alexander Technique", nor is it all of the processes required to do the Alexander Technique, but it is a mental skill we must all acquire if we are ever to do Alexander's work.

Alexander does not tell us that it was the information which he gained from this particular practice which was of value but it was "the experience [which he] gained in giving these directions (which) proved of great value when the time came ... to consider how to put (these directions) into practice"[95] By performing this process for considerable amounts of time and with great discipline, by projecting his directive guidance commands without attempting to "do" them (or even to relate them to the end he wished to gain), he acquired another mental discipline necessary to learn about and perform his work. What is more, without these skills, he could not have gone on to discover the skill of Additive Thinking, perhaps the single most important key to understanding and mastering Alexander's work.

---

[95] *ibid.*, p. 41.

Chapter 13
ADDITIVE THINKING

THROUGH THE EXPERIENCE he gained by practicing the skills of both inhibition and of giving his directions without attempting to "do" them, Alexander began to acquire a new mental discipline, a discipline unlike any other before it, a skill and understanding that I call the Principle of Additive Thinking.

Formally stated, through his experience of projecting his "directions" without attempting to "do" them, Alexander learned:

1. that "before attempting to "do" even the first part of the new "means-whereby" which [he] had decided to employ in order to gain [his] end ..., [he] must give the directions preparatory to the doing of this first part very many times;

2. that [he] must *continue* to give the directions preparatory to the doing of the first part while [he] gave the directions preparatory to the doing of the second part;

3. that [he] must *continue* to give the directions preparatory to the doing of the first and second parts while [he] gave the directions preparatory to the doing of the third part; and so on for the doing of the fourth and other parts as required.[96]

The importance of learning how to do this particular procedure cannot be overemphasized.

It took Alexander most of his narrative to get to the point where he chose to forsake directive guidance by any form of feeling for the directive guidance of his reasoning processes. As we have seen, the first procedure that he introduced for the implementation of this new and reasoned source of directive guidance – the Three Part Process of Protocol Design – was not entirely unique to his work.

Although Alexander believed that thinking out a reasonable means by which a certain end may be achieved was the one great principle upon which man's advancement in civilization depended and although very few people analyze the conditions present, reason out appropriate procedures for gaining an end, and then think about the processes they wish to perform instead of the product they wish to gain; behaving in this way does not require knowledge of Alexander and his work to be used. In fact, most good, modern athletic training and fine arts coaching programs use this very design as a basis for their procedures. It is only

---

96   Alexander, F.M., *The Use of the Self.* Gollancz, London, 1985, p. 41.

when Alexander begins to apply his new mental skills of constructive dissociation through inhibition and the projection of directive orders without attempting
to "do" them that he begins to learn how to organize his thought processes
according to the Principle of Additive Thinking. It is only when he begins to
organize his thought processes according to the Principle of Additive Thinking
that he begins to adopt procedures that are truly contrary to any procedure "in
which man's instinctive processes have been drilled."[97]

It would be inappropriate in an introductory text to discuss the topic of Additive Thinking fully in the manner that it deserves. That discussion would be
more appropriately performed elsewhere.[98] There are, however, a number of
points from that discussion that I believe would be of value to mention here.

*   *   *   *   *

First of all, it is important to remember that the discovery of how one's thinking
may be organized additively was a direct result of carrying out experiments in
inhibition and the projection of directions without attempting to "do" them.
These two mental skills can only be acquired by carrying out that same kind of
disciplined practice as Alexander did for prolonged periods of time. A high
degree of accomplishment in these particular mental skills is necessary first to
the understanding of, and then the implementation of, this new principle of
Additive Thinking. Therefore, this kind of prolonged skill-building practice must
be carried out in order to enjoy success in the work.

Secondly, in class we have found that the nature of Additive Thinking can be
summarized in a simple sentence: Additive Thinking is repetitive, additive, and
successive.

That the process of Additive Thinking is repetitive is obvious from the very
first part of the procedure that Alexander describes. He tells us that, "I must give
the directions preparatory to the doing of this first part very many times." Even
if you were only going to give one direction, you would have to give it very
many times. Therefore, the first characteristic of Additive Thinking is that it is
repetitive.

The second characteristic of Additive Thinking is that it is additive. When
one progresses from the giving of the directions preparatory to the doing of the
first part of a protocol for the performance of a given activity to the giving of the
directions preparatory to the doing of the second part of that protocol, one CON-
TINUES to give the directions for the first part WHILE adding in the directions for

---

[97] *ibid.*, p. 46.

[98] See Volume II of *The Alexander Commentaries*.

the second part. In this way, the repetitive aspect of this manner of thinking is emphasized, and the additive nature of this manner of thought can be seen.

To "think" in this manner, one CONTINUES to repeat the directions – individually and repetitively – that have gone before as the new directions are "added in". One CONTINUES to repeat and to give the directions preparatory to the doing of the first part of the protocol as one ADDS IN the directions preparatory to the doing of the second part. Then one CONTINUES to repeat and to give the directions preparatory to the doing of the first and second parts of the protocol – individually and repetitively – as one ADDS IN the directions preparatory to the doing of the third part. Then one CONTINUES to give the directions preparatory to the doing of the first, second, and third parts – individually and repetitively – as one ADDS IN the directions preparatory to the doing of the fourth part, and so on.

In this way the process of Additive Thinking can be seen as both repetitive and additive.

The third aspect of the process of Additive Thinking is at least as important as the other two. Additive Thinking is successive, i.e., it occurs in a sequence.

Every movement that we perform is sequential. Like a well-made play, it has a beginning, a middle, and an end. Similarly, the "thinking" which produces such a movement is sequential as well. If it were not, the order of the firing of the muscles and the movement that these firings caused would be "out-of-sequence" for the intended movement. In a large sense, this "out-of-sequence-ness" is what we mean when we say that a movement is mal-coordinated.

Alexander discovered that the best way the actual movement can match the intended movement is for the sequence of the commands projected to match the sequence of movements required to perform the intended movement. Once one has decided on what movement to perform, and analyzed the conditions present, and reasoned out an appropriate protocol for response, then, the sequence of the "thinking" which is projected must match the sequence of events required to perform the protocol. In addition, Alexander tells us that even after a particular part of the protocol has been performed, the whole of the protocol sequence – including the directions preparatory to the doing of parts already completed – must continue to be projected.

Thus it can be seen that the process of Additive Thinking is repetitive, additive, and successive.

*   *   *   *   *

Alexander tells us that even after he had become familiar with this process of additively combining the giving of his directions, it was still necessary to "continue this process [of training my thinking] in my practice for a considerable time before actually attempting to employ the new 'means-whereby' for the purpose of speaking."[99] Even after he had spent all of those days and weeks and, sometimes, even months, in practice, leading up to this procedural discovery, he had to continue to practice giving himself these directions many times without attempting to "do" any of them. Even after all the mental practice required to create this new procedure, Alexander still had to practice this new way of thinking for a considerable time before putting it to use, "before attempting to employ the new 'means-whereby' for the purpose of speaking."[100]

In other words, this new manner of thought takes both time and practice to develop and then even more time "practicing" before it can be put into constructive and consistent use. We know this is true because it took Alexander a "considerable" amount of time to practice and develop it. Therefore, it is likely that it will take all of us a "considerable" amount of time to practice and develop it for ourselves.

Alexander also told us that "anyone who carries out (these new mental disciplines) faithfully while trying to gain an end will find that he is acquiring a new experience in what he calls 'thinking.'"[101] The new practitioner will be acquiring a new experience in thinking because this part of Alexander's technique – the Principle of Additive Thinking – requires the creation and implementation of an entirely new and different way of consciously organizing and sending out movement protocol commands.

Because Additive Thinking is a new skill, it will take time to learn. It took Alexander time to learn it. It took everyone who came after Alexander time to learn it. It will take you time to learn it as well.

It will also take time for you to refine it.

If we think of someone who has become a concert pianist, we can ask the question: When did this person learn to play the piano? The only answer that really makes any sense is that he or she learned to play the piano the moment when the relationship between striking the keys and making a sound was established. Once you understand that when you push the keys down, the piano makes a noise, you know how to play the piano. Everything that comes after that moment is merely a refinement and development of that first piece of information.

Therefore, it will take time and practice for you to refine your ability to do this new kind of thinking.

Just as it did everyone else.

*   *   *   *   *

---

[99] *ibid.*, p. 42.

[100] *ibid.*, p. 42.

[101] *ibid.*, p. 42. The quotation marks are Alexander's.

There is a step in the development of your ability to think in this new way that will probably prove most difficult for you. By saying this, I am not trying to cloud your thinking with negative ideas. I am merely passing on what Alexander told us was true of every student he had ever known. In fact, this step of acquiring the ability to think additively while working to a reasoned plan is so important to learning Alexander's work, I believe that it is one of the distinguishing differences that makes this work a skill to be acquired rather than information to be learned.

When one is simply learning information, the most important step is the step from not having the information to having it. We can think of this as the step from zero to one, where zero represents the state of ignorance with regard to the information and one represents the state of possession of the information.

In the acquisition of a skill to be performed, however, not only are there often many different bits or pieces of information to be acquired, but the possession of all of this information does not mean that the skill itself has been learned. For example, there is a tremendous difference between having word-perfect recall of an accurate book on the skills of bronco busting and surviving an actual ride on one of these beasts.

The acquisition of a skill has to do with the ability to be in *practical* possession of at least one bit of significant information, and then being able to add to it – in a *practical* manner – succeeding bits of significant information. In this way, it can be seen that the most important step in the acquisition of a skill is not simply coming into possession of new information, the step from zero to one; but the ability to add in each successive new step to the ability you already had. In other words, the most important step in the acquisition of a skill is not the step from zero to one, but rather the step from one to two.

Similarly, the most difficult step to learn while practicing the Principle of Additive Thinking is not the step from zero to one – giving one direction – but rather the step from one to two – learning how to continue to give the first direction while adding in the second. Alexander tells us that anyone can project one direction (the step from zero to one) and focus his or her mind repetitively on just one of these directions. They could probably even string several of these single directions together into an increasingly long "single" direction and focus on that. But it is the next step, when one tries "to continue to give (the first) direction as we project the second"[102] wherein the difficulty begins.

To be able to do this requires a new and different way of thinking. Once you have learned to perform this step and you are able to continue to project one direction while projecting the second (wholly, completely, and independent of the first), however, you will have created within yourself the template for each

---

[102] *ibid.*, p. 42.

succeeding stage of development. Once you have taught yourself how to continue to project one direction while projecting the second, you can more easily learn to continue to project the first and second directions as you add in the third, and each succeeding, direction. In time, you will acquire the skill and ability to project – separately, simultaneously, and continuously – all of the directions necessary for carrying out your reasoned protocols for the gaining of your ends.

Many students seem to reach this point in their training only to become discouraged at how slowly progress is initially made. I don't know why they are discouraged.

In the first place, to proceed to the next level of development means that you have to discipline your thinking until you acquire and master a skill in a manner of directing yourself in activity that is contrary to any manner of directive thought that has been used previously throughout all of evolution. In addition, Alexander himself points out in his narrative that every student he has ever known has stumbled when coming up against this very point.

I must confess that I cannot tell you precisely what Additive Thinking is. Nor do I know precisely what changes in thinking will have to happen in you for this additive ability to take place. What I do know is that every one of my students who has taken the challenge of learning to think additively and who has worked on this skill in the way that Alexander describes has been able to do it.

Some a little slow. Some a little fast.

Everyone only just a little in the beginning.

But, every student who has ever taken this challenge and passed through the step from one (the ability to give one direction) to two (the ability to continue to give the first direction while giving the second) has – over time and with practice – acquired a constantly increasing capacity to do this kind of thinking in an increasingly successful way and with very gratifying results.

*   *   *   *   *

Once Alexander had worked on this new mental skill for several periods of considerable time, he "believed [that he] had practised the "means-whereby" long enough, and [he] started to try and employ them for the purpose of speaking."[103] The only problem he had at this point was that he failed more often than he succeeded.

He was frustrated by this turn of events because he knew he was attempting to prevent his habitual responses. He knew he was saying his directions repeatedly and sufficiently. He thought he was doing everything that he needed to do

---

[103] *ibid.*, p. 42.

in the way that he needed to do it – and still he did not enjoy success! He was doing everything as it seemed he should, but he still continued to fail at a very high rate. Most of us can relate personally to this experience in learning this work, but in order to solve this new dilemma, Alexander did something most of us prefer to avoid. He went back to the beginning and reconsidered everything once more.

Upon reflection, he saw that the times that he failed were those times in which he had failed to prevent his old wrong use by failing to prevent his old misdirection. From this he concluded that the instinctive misdirection that he had formerly used to guide himself in activity still dominated[104] his new, conscious, reasoning direction.[105] Because of the faith he had both in the reasoning and analysis that had brought him to this point in his adventure as well as the faith he had in the new means for change that his reasoning had suggested, he decided to look elsewhere for the cause of his failures.

First, like almost all of us, he blamed himself for his failures – as though his personal shortcomings were the root cause of his lack of success. When he realized that this contention did not have the power to advance his investigation

---

[104] A number of people have criticized me for introducing what they see as a concept of conflict that is implied by my use of the various forms of the word "dominate". Apparently, they are in possession of a kinder, gentler consciousness and manner of thought that they feel is threatened by these terms of conflict. Further, they say to me that by introducing this idea of conflict into my work, I doom my students to a much darker view of the world than it deserves, and as a result my students miss all that the world can be. Whether or not my students are doomed is an issue I will put aside for the moment long enough to remind these critics that I did not introduce the concept of "domination"; Alexander did. In fact, almost every idea which I put forward in any of my efforts can be found somewhere in the literature of this work.

[105] These two sentences (lines 702-9 in the Gollancz edition) report the final major change in understanding that Alexander shares in his narrative. It is without question the most important step he takes in his journey. For having abandoned the pursuit of kinesthetic re-education as his means of change, he finally puts aside consideration of habitual wrong use as the dominating force within him. At last he sees that what dominates his actions is not any set pattern of physical response, but his manner of directing himself in activity. When he is dominated by his instinctive misdirection, he is unable to change as he desires. To the degree he is able to dominate his instinctive manner of direction with his new and reasoned conscious direction, he will succeed.

Some have questioned my judgment that this step is the most important step in the journey. My only defense is that Alexander thought it was so important that he wrote "and this was of the utmost importance" in reference to this step. Careful study of Alexander's writing shows that, as a writer, he was precise, conservative, and economical. I know his sentences are often long and complex but the concepts conveyed are just as often immense and simultaneous. For a writer such as he was to take the time and space to leave a flashing neon day-glow trail marker like the phrase "and this was of the utmost importance" is sufficient proof to me of the tremendous importance of the step to which he refers.

(even if it were true), he looked elsewhere for the source of his continuing failures.

The only other possible cause for his failures that he could think of would be if, at the critical moment of taking his planning into activity, he had failed to continue with his intention to change his manner of use in the performance of his activities. He wondered if, instead of "continuing to project the directions (for the new use he had reasoned out) in their proper sequence," he reverted to "the instinctive misdirection of [his] old habitual use," i.e., to his old way of doing things, in spite of his "feeling" or believing he had stopped using these old command protocols. Further investigation proved that he did still use his old command protocols even though he "felt" that he had stopped. In other words, far more often than not, he reverted to his old habitual patterns of directive guidance – and, hence, his old way of doing things – as he went into activity.

Upon further reflection, Alexander saw that this dominance of his instinctive misdirection could hardly have been otherwise. Prior to his investigation, this process of instinctive misdirection was the only direction that he had ever used, and the use of himself by this mode of direction had become so familiar that it now felt "natural and right." Moreover, by disciplining himself to project conscious directions in a sequence, he was trying to follow a new and different process of guidance, one in which neither he nor anyone else had any experience at all. In this way, the power of the racial inheritance of relying on instinctive direction was made greater by the racial inexperience of projecting directions consciously, particularly projecting directions consciously in a sequence.[106] In order to succeed against the strength of these two racial tendencies, Alexander decided that he needed to close any remaining loopholes in his plan for change.

*   *   *   *   *

When Alexander had finally seen the importance and inherent difficulty of the task he had set himself, it led him to see the final obstacle that he had erected in his own way.

He writes to us that "[he] had recognized much earlier that [he] ought not to trust to [his] feeling for the direction of [his] use, but (that he) had never fully realized all that this implied."[107] He had failed to recognize that his standards for judgment were based on his sense of what felt right in a movement and that what "felt right" was determined by what was familiar. Because only those movements that he habitually made would feel familiar, any immediate attempt to

---

[106] It is clear from the context that Alexander's use of the term "racial" has more to do with the characteristics of the human species as a whole rather than the specific characteristics of any human subgroup.

[107] _ibid._, p. 44.

apply these old standards of judgment to any new movement in any meaningful way would doom his efforts to change. It was this re-initiation of his old misdirection as an unwanted by-product of immediately judging his success by means of how the movement felt to him that was the final loophole that he had to learn how to close.

Obviously, he reasoned, any new way of doing things must feel different from the old way of doing them. If – through familiarity – the old way of doing things "felt right", then the new way of doing them was bound to feel "wrong". "I now had to face the fact," Alexander told us, "that in all my attempts during these past months I had been trying to employ a new use of myself which was bound to feel wrong, at the same time trusting to my feeling of what was right (based on past familiarity and his old manner of misdirection) to tell me whether I was employing (the new way of doing things) or not."[108]

The important issue with regards to feelings in this case is not so much an issue of the relative trustworthiness of the feelings being used as an issue of self-defeat, a self-defeat caused by the re-initiation of the old way of doing things in order to implement the use of familiar feelings for the purpose of judging current progress. Here he was, trying to employ a new use of himself, "while for the purpose of this attempt [he] was actually bringing into play [his] old habitual use (by means of reverting) to [his] instinctive misdirection. Small wonder that this attempt had proved futile!"[109] The problem, therefore, was not how trustworthy his feelings were, but that he was using his feelings for judging current progress in his movements. The use of his old familiar feelings for immediate judgment re-initiated his old instinctive misdirection that, in turn, re-initiated his old familiar responses.

*   *   *   *   *

In order to do things in a new way, Alexander decided that he must employ a new and reasoned manner of directing himself in activity. By allowing his immediate and on-going interpretation of his old "feelings" to be a part of his efforts, he re-initiated (and reverted to) his old manner of misdirection associated with reliance upon familiar feelings as a guide. As soon as this old manner of direction was re-initiated, the strength of this old misdirection – with respect to the strength of the newer and reasoned direction of himself – dominated his new, reasoned direction and reverting to his old manner of misdirection became practically irresistible. In other words, you cannot use the directions associated with your old manner of performing an activity in any way whatsoever while installing a new manner of directing yourself without getting caught up in your old manner of misdirection.

---

[108] *ibid.*, p. 44.

[109] *ibid.*, pp. 44-5.

Once your old manner of directing yourself is initiated, or re-initiated, the game is over.

You can't use something to perform the act of not using it.

You can't use your old manner of directing your use in activity to prevent yourself from directing yourself in that way.

You can't even use your old manner of directing yourself in activity to judge how well you are directing yourself in your new way because the old manner of directing yourself that would be used to make the judgment is so powerful that it is liable to dominate any new means of direction.

To succeed in making changes in yourself, you must find a way to break out of this cycle. Finding a way to break out of this cycle became Alexander's goal. He decided that if he were going to enjoy success in making changes in the way he did things, he would have to find a way of directing himself that did not re-initiate his old manner of directing himself for either guidance or judgment. He decided that he had to find a way to guarantee that he could discipline himself to use his new manner of direction throughout the performance of his activities and it was this that led him to the fifth mental discipline required to do his work. As he told us in his story, "I now saw that if I was ever to succeed in making the changes in use I desired, I must subject the processes directing my use to a new experience, the experience, that is, *of being dominated by reasoning instead of by feeling.*"[110]

---

[110] *ibid.*, p. 45.

Chapter 14

GENUINE TRUST

WHEN I LOOK at what Alexander said in his books, I am most impressed with what he said about the importance of relying on one's reasoning as a source of guidance rather than one's feeling-sense interpretation. The "mysteries" surrounding this issue must make up over half of the questions I am asked in teaching. In watching people's reactions while I answer these questions, I continue to notice certain common responses.

People are so accustomed to the belief that they are "guided by feelings" and so committed to the process of judging their results immediately upon the completion of a given act (or sooner) as part of their usual protocols that they become quite uncomfortable with the suggestion that they stop, slow down, and see what they are really doing.

After much discussion and sufficient practical demonstration, they seem willing to put aside their belief in their "Feeling Guidance Mechanism" and to try to "think" a little more. In spite of this, however, almost none of them are willing to stop using their old feelings to judge how successful they are in making changes and even fewer of them are willing to rely completely on their reasoning processes to bring them safely to their ends.

*   *   *   *   *

When Alexander admits that he had failed to realize all of the implications of not trusting to his feeling sense, he begins a section of his story whose importance cannot be stated too strongly.

Because of its long term familiarity, Alexander reasoned that the sensory experience associated with his old use would not only FEEL right when he moved in a familiar way, but performing the act in this way would be judged by him as BEING right which would, in turn, make him feel as though "HE" was RIGHT.

The sensory experience associated with his new use would be generated by different actions and movements from those he had done before, thereby exciting different static position recognition sensors. As a result, performing actions with his new use would necessarily send back different feeling-sense data to his central nervous system. This would enhance the probability that performing the same act in this new way would feel different from performing it in the customary way.[111]

And what was true for Alexander is true for all of us. Because the act "feels" different when performed in this new way, and because the judgment of "feeling" associated with performing the act in the old way is that the old way IS right, performing the act in this new way is judged by most of us as BEING WRONG.

It is not simply enough to recognize that the movement performed in this way would FEEL wrong. Feeling in these cases is only the means to reaching a decision about how we are doing. We leap from the "feeling right"-ness of a familiar action to the conclusion that we ourselves ARE RIGHT – when we move in that way. Because our new manner of movement is being judged against the "kinesthetic coordinates" of previous performances, and because we have invested our relative scale of feeling-sense interpretation with an almost absolute authority to tell us how we are doing,[112] any new movement which does not match up with the feeling sense of previous performances not only FEELS WRONG, but is judged to BE wrong.

When Alexander looked further into his situation, he saw that for months he had been trying to employ his new use while at the same time relying upon the by-products of his old instinctive misdirection and manner of use to judge his success. In the process of using his old misdirection to judge the quality and nature of his performance, he had re-initiated this misdirection as a source of directive guidance. By using his old instinctive misdirection and manner of use to judge his success in carrying out his new directions, he brought his old misdirection into play. No wonder he failed more often than not in changing the manner of his use! By bringing into operation the very thing he was trying to prevent, he was guaranteeing the enduring success of his continual failure.

*   *   *   *   *

It was at this point that Alexander took the step that eliminates forever any claim that his work involves the process of directly making his feeling-sense interpre-

---

[111] It is important to note that this is only a probability. For instance, I have taught a large number of introductory lessons in which the change in appearance and manner of movement in an individual has been dramatic enough to elicit gasps of surprise and amazement from the other students in the class only to have the individual having the lesson report that he felt about the same. In these cases, the students who are having the lesson notice very few, if any, differences as a result of our work together, even though the changes were dramatic enough to evoke responses from the rest of the class. Consider for a moment the strength of the ruling conceptual monarchy in an individual who can undergo large transformational experiences that go undetected by his feeling-sense interpretation.

[112] All of this in spite of the fact that feelings themselves are not absolute. See pp. 75-76.

tation trustworthy once more. It was at this point that Alexander unequivocally claimed that one should rely only on his reasoning as a source and means of guidance, or, as he put it, "If I ever was to succeed in making the changes in use I desired, I must subject the processes directing my new use to a new experience, the experience, that is, of being dominated by reasoning instead of by feeling."[113] To say that again: Alexander said we MUST be "dominated by reasoning instead of by feeling."

The issue here is not one of reliability or trustworthiness. It is a matter of choosing what you will use to guide the processes directing your use. To put it in terms of the Decision Game, between (left hand) Reasoning and (right hand) Feeling – even completely trustworthy Feeling – which should I use to direct my new use while doing the Alexander Technique? Alexander makes the answer to this question so clear we don't even have to Score this Decision. All we have to do is read!

"If I was ever to succeed in making the changes in use I desired, I must subject the processes directing my use to a new experience, the experience, that is, of being dominated by reasoning instead of by feeling".

The correct answer according to Alexander is (left hand) Reasoning!

The trustworthiness of the feeling sense is not the issue (and therefore not a process we should directly pursue), because the feeling sense is not going to be used in the performance of Alexander's technique for changing the use of the self in activity.

It won't be used for guidance.

It won't be used for immediate judgment.

It won't be used at all.

What would be the point of developing a trustworthy feeling sense if, in order to do this work, we are not going to use it?[114]

Alexander decided that he must use his reasoning to dominate "the processes directing his use"[115] by reasoning. He decided that he must stop using his feelings – trustworthy and otherwise – as a source of guidance or as a means of immediately judging his performance because both procedures reinitiated his old

---

[113] Alexander, F.M., *The Use of the Self*. Gollancz, London, 1985, p. 45.

[114] In Alexander's work, feelings are not going to be used even if they become trustworthy again. Marjory Barlow reminds us of this when she quotes FM as saying, "A time will come when you can trust your feelings, but by then you won't want to because you'll have something much more reliable." (Barlow, Marjory, *An Examined Life in conversation with Trevor Allan Davies*. Mornum Time Press, Berkeley, 2002, p. 60.)

[115] *ibid.*, p. 45.

habitual patterns of directive guidance and misdirection. But this understanding carried even greater implications.

As Alexander wrote, "This meant that I must be prepared to carry on with any procedure I had reasoned out as best for my purpose, even though that procedure *might feel wrong.*"[116] Because the carrying out of the new procedure would FEEL wrong, Alexander would get the impression that "HE" was WRONG in doing the procedure in this way. If Alexander was ever to be successful in changing his manner of use in activity, then he must put aside all of his judgments based on feeling, and stay with the new procedures he had reasoned out, even when his feelings were screaming out that "HE" was WRONG to do so! Even when his feelings were confusing him with sensations of pain or of cramping or of being pulled out of shape. Even when his feelings were confusing him with sensations of being lengthened or of pleasure or of ease or of lightness. Alexander decided that if he was ever to succeed he must stay with the procedures he had reasoned out as being best suited for his purpose no matter how moving in this new and different way felt.

*   *   *   *   *

By changing from a reliance on feelings as a guide or a source of immediate judgment to a reliance on the procedures he had reasoned out as best for his purpose, he had to change completely the person he used to be. He had to shift from relying on his "feelings" and his sense of BEING RIGHT for guidance, to relying on the use of his conscious, reasoning mind to see and project what each activity required, to plan an appropriate strategy, and to send out the commands necessary for the implementation of this strategy. To achieve reliance upon his reasoning processes would take something more than just the desire to carry out his new directions. To achieve reliance upon his reasoning processes would require a commitment in defiance of both his past and his past feelings. To achieve reliance upon his reasoning processes would require trust – a genuine trust.

"In other words, my trust in my reasoning processes to bring me safely to my "end" must be a genuine trust, not a half-trust needing the assurance *of feeling right* as well."[117]

This genuine trust in his reasoning processes to bring him safely to his end is the final piece in the puzzle of Alexander's technique for constructive change. It is the final mental discipline he had to learn. Without this trust and the complete abandonment of reliance upon the feeling sense for either guidance or immediate judgment that this trust implies, no one can truly raise his mastery of Alexan-

---

[116] *ibid.*, p. 45.

[117] *ibid.*, p. 45.

der's work onto the plane of conscious guidance and control. Without the domination of reasoning and the abandonment of feeling as a guide, one would be doomed to a spiraling maze in which one enjoyed increasingly sophisticated forms of better seeming posture, better seeming movement, better seeming performance, etc. – without ever really having to change.

Genuine trust is the final key to learning the Alexander Technique. It is the final mental discipline that powers the processes of fundamental change that lie at the center of Alexander's work.

*   *   *   *   *

Students are always trying to catch me in a fault.

Time does not permit a listing of all of the different ways in which they have tried. One of their favorite ploys, however, is to try to ask me questions that they believe are impossible to answer or a series of questions that will demonstrate some inconsistency in what I say, or that will demonstrate that I had been wrong in something that I had previously said. The fact that they rarely succeed[118] does not disturb them as much as my reaction does when they are successful.

While I might have a number of different reactions to being proven wrong – surprise, disbelief, disagreement, etc. – my dominant reaction is one of delight. I have worked so hard and so long on this material that any further clue or insight into it's meaning is welcome.

"But, doesn't it bother you that you were wrong?" my students persist.

Not really. I've been wrong before. I will be wrong again. Oh, sure, sometimes I'm embarrassed to find out that I could still think and act as though I were that stupid, but I know that I will be wrong again and that being wrong isn't all that important.

Years ago, I was at an audition for the Ringling Brother's Clown College. We were all seated around the center ring and, as part of their audition procedure; a group of clowns were doing some skits. It was a pleasure to be this close to the clowns as they worked because for the first time I realized that the scripts they used had dialogue and that the dialogue was, in many ways, funnier than the actions.

At one point, one of the clowns gave a cue for the next part of the script. The other clown apparently confused the cue in this script for a similar cue in a second script. The first clown gave the cue from script A and the second clown responded with the answer from script B, an answer that made it impossible for

---

[118] The only reason why I am usually able to answer their questions and objections well is because I have already answered almost all of the same questions and objections before, either for myself or for other students.

the first script to continue. The first clown then repeated the cue from script A and the second clown repeated the answer from script B. Then the first clown forcefully repeated the cue from script A once more only to be answered with an equally adamant reply from script B.

This exchange continued for several more repetitions and with several variations until finally it dawned upon the second clown that she was in the wrong script. In response to the first clown's next cue, she said, "Faux pas," and then simply gave the correct verbal response and the skit moved on as if there had been no interruption.

I have always admired the second clown's response. She was wrong. She realized it. She acknowledged it and went on.

She didn't make a big deal out of it. She didn't apologize profusely. She didn't tear her clothes and beg forgiveness. She didn't feel she was less of a person. She just acknowledged her fault and went on.

The fact that she had made a mistake wasn't important.

The fact that she went on was.

*   *   *   *   *

There is nothing wrong with being wrong.

We are all wrong sometimes, just as we are all right at other times.

We all make mistakes. We all make good decisions. We all do well. We all do poorly.

Most of the time our errors have little consequence and, even when there are consequences, it is only rarely that the problems caused can't be fixed. But, too often, too many of us treat every little mistake as a catastrophe. I know this feeling of disaster comes about as a result of feeling challenged and insecure, but even if we are challenged to the core, there is no way that we can avoid being wrong at times.

But, that's okay, because there is nothing wrong with being wrong. Just as there is nothing wrong with failing. What is important in life is not failure or success. All of us will enjoy both throughout our lives. What is important in life lies in having an idea of what we want to do and be, and performing the steps necessary to make these dreams come true.

If we are satisfied with ourselves and our lives, then there really is no need for us to change. The vast majority of people I encounter fit into this category. If you question them, they will tell you that they might want a bigger TV or a longer vacation or their backs to hurt a little less after gardening. But, if you show them what they would need to do to reach these goals, much more often than not they will tell you that they would just as soon let it go.

For the rest of us, we believe that as good as our lives have become, there may be something more. As much as we have achieved, there may be more for us to do. As much as we have matured and grown as individuals, there may be a better person yet to come. For us, the acquisition of new knowledge and new ways to improve ourselves becomes a joy that surpasses the cost of the acquisition. For us, the potential of learning how to change in constructive and valuable ways is worth the price in time, money, and discipline required. For us, the value of picking up new tools and ideas that will help us reach our goals is worth the heartache and momentary insecurity of putting down what we have believed and held dear.

But, it is not easy. It will take time. It will take effort. It will take discipline. It will take trust.

It will take the same kind of genuine trust about which Alexander speaks. The kind of genuine trust to put aside your "stuff" – the things which you believe or feel to be true – long enough to put into action the procedures you have reasoned out as best for your purpose.

"But, how will I know I am doing it right?" my students plead.

By measuring your performance against the concepts of your intent long after the action has been performed. Then, you will make judgments about your degree of success. Then, you will make judgments about how well you carried out your plan. Then, you will make judgments about how appropriate your plan was to your goals. But, judgments do not have to be judgmental. Neither do they have to occur NOW. LATER will be fine.

"But, how will I know I am doing it right?"

You won't. You can't.

I'm not even sure that there is a right way to do this work.

I do know that there are a number of discoveries that Alexander made, a number of procedures that he devised, a number of skills that he acquired through the implementation of those procedures, and a number of mental disciplines that he developed. I also know that if I will simply do the same things that Alexander did, follow the same procedures, acquire the same skills, discipline my mind in the same ways – that is, as long as I "do what he did" – I cannot help but acquire at least the same degree of conscious guidance and control which he enjoyed.

"But, how will I know I am doing it right?"

It's not as important to be right, as it is to be consistent and persevere.

In beginning classes, we sometimes talk about how "thinking" leads to movement and movement leads to change.[119] We talk about how people are

---

[119] See the Box Chart for Beginners in Appendix B.

always in a hurry to take some new impression or feeling or understanding back into the commands that they are using to direct themselves rather than staying with the ordered directions they have reasoned out as best for their purpose.

In doing this work, there are certain things you will train yourself to "think" as you go into an activity. If the activity is successful, you will "think" these same things again as you go into another attempt.[120] If the activity you have performed is unsuccessful, however, YOU MUST "think" THESE SAME THINGS AGAIN. That's the part that students rarely understand.

*   *   *   *   *

Over the years, students' names have been attached to the various titles assigned to the principles we talk about in class, as a reward for meritorious valor, insight, or stupidity. Since I assign the titles, my name is attached to one of the more important of the laws, one that is tricky to understand but well worth the effort.

Dr. Don's Law says that results are no criteria for success.

The easiest level of this law to understand, and the most relevant aspect to our present discussion, is summed up in the sports cliché: "It's not whether you win or lose, but how you play the game." Someone whose attitude towards success reflects that of Vince Lombardi[121] will not be comfortable with this concept. Neither will they learn Alexander's work. They will be so busy trying to win that they will be unable to see the causal relationship between their manner of performance and the probability of success.

Yes, the Green Bay Packers were the dominant American football team of their era. Yes, their passion for success did reflect their coach's passion, but the way in which they achieved success had more to do with the strategies and procedures written about by one of the team's best players, a man named Jerry Kramer.

Jerry Kramer was acknowledged at the time as the best offensive lineman to play the game of American football. For years his form and techniques of blocking were taught as the standard for the profession. Towards the end of his career he wrote a series of articles that described his procedures. The article that caught my attention was the first one in which he described how to take the proper stance before a play begins.

---

[120] If you go into a different activity, there are certain parts of these commands that you will leave unchanged, making only the few changes required to change the task-specific "shape" of your activity.

[121] Lombardi was the head coach of the Green Bay Packers and made them the most successful team in the history of professional American football. Lombardi was quoted as saying, "Winning isn't everything – it's the only thing!" In his defense, Lombardi also said, "We never lost a game. We just ran out of time."

Kramer said that after all those years of success as a high school player and all those years of success as a college player and all of those years of success as a professional player, the hardest thing he had to do every fall was to re-learn how to get into his three-point stance, the starting position he assumed at the beginning of every offensive play. For the first three or four weeks of preseason practice, he would spend hours each day turning around, trotting seven yards, and getting down into his three point stance. Once he felt comfortable in his stance, he would stand up, turn around, trot seven yards, and get down into his stance again.

The three-point stance, so named for putting one hand on the ground while bending over, was the basic position from which all of his other techniques followed. Until he had reacquired the skill of getting down into this stance easily, consistently, and at will, he had no foundation upon which to rebuild the rest of his techniques. Once he had learned again how to get back into this stance, he would add in each next part of the process, one step at a time, until he had reacquired a comfortable proficiency in all of his superlative skills.[122]

In doing this work, there are certain things you will train yourself to "think" as you go into activity. If the activity is successful, you will "think" these same things again as you go into another attempt. But even if the activity you have performed is unsuccessful, YOU MUST "think" THESE SAME THINGS AGAIN.

The reason why your immediate judgment of your success is relatively unimportant is that your degree of immediate success is irrelevant compared to the importance of the process of discipline you are trying to develop. If your plan is appropriate to reaching your goals and you develop the mental discipline necessary to carry out your plan, in time, you cannot avoid success. It is inevitable.

No matter what your degree of success, however, there are certain things you will train yourself to "think" as you go into activity. If the activity is successful, you will "think" these same things again as you go into another attempt. If the activity you perform is unsuccessful, YOU MUST "think" THESE SAME THINGS AGAIN, because your task at the moment is to train your thinking – not to have success.

Yes, I know that eventually you will have to make judgments about the effectiveness of the procedures you are using. There may even be times when you

---

[122] Usually when I tell this story to students they seem surprised that a Hall of Fame player, someone recognized by experts in his fields and his peers as being one of the best, would have to take so long and work so hard each year just to learn how to stand. I point out to them that it was partly because he took all of this time following these constructive procedures that he became such a good player. I tell them to remember that amateurs use practice sessions to focus in on those things they already do well. Champions always spend time practicing the things they do the worst, particularly those techniques that are fundamental to the building up of other skills.

will want to experiment with the way you are doing these procedures or even the procedures themselves. Whenever you find yourself wanting to set aside the procedures we have talked about in favor of some "new and improved" way of doing this work, however, I ask that you keep three things in mind before you make any change.

First of all, people say that Alexander was a brilliant and insightful genius. But, in learning this work, even this "brilliant genius" had to perform experiments that lasted for days and weeks and sometimes even months without changing his procedures. Perhaps trying something for a few times in class without success is not enough practice for us "non-geniuses" to acquire these same skills. Therefore, immediate lack of success is not enough reason to change your procedures or give up.

Secondly, Alexander applied the Principle of Unavoidability to all of the changes in procedure that he made. He only changed his procedures when the results of exhaustive, long-term experimentation and the reasoning he applied to those results made changing his procedures unavoidable.[123]

Most importantly, we don't have to worry, guess, or wonder whether the processes Alexander outlined work or not. They do work. We know it, both because of our experiences in class and because of the success that Alexander enjoyed with them. We also don't have to re-invent or improve the work. The mental disciplines that Alexander pointed out to us will work just fine without our help.

When my colleagues ask me what I think about their new discoveries or the way somebody or other is teaching the work, I tell them that as soon as I have mastered everything that Alexander showed us, I will look into the improvements and innovations. When they ask me about the best ways to project the directions or the best design to use for the creation of the most efficient condition of mechanical advantage possible, I tell them that as soon as I have learned to eliminate all of the interferences I am creating in myself in my manner of thinking and movement, I will worry about how to invent something more efficient.

All we have to do to gain the advantages Mr. Alexander enjoyed is acquire the same skills and mental disciplines that he had, in the way that he acquired them, and then apply these same processes in all of our activities, in the way that he applied them. If we do this, we will not be able to avoid acquiring a level of conscious guidance and control at least as good as Alexander's.

In this work, there are certain things you will train yourself to "think" as you go into activity. If the activity is successful, you will "think" these same things again as you go into another attempt. If the activity you have performed is

---

[123] See Appendix A for a more complete discussion.

unsuccessful, in order to work on your mental discipline, YOU MUST "think" THESE SAME THINGS AGAIN.

Just as it is a poor trust that requires the assurance of feeling right, it is an even poorer trust that requires immediate gratification or success.

*   *   *   *   *

In all the travels, work, and study that I have done, I have never found a tool or an idea as valuable as Alexander's work. In all of the disciplines I've explored and all of these years that I've searched, I have never found a better way for people to make constructive changes in themselves. Most importantly, in all of these years of experiments and investigation, I have never seen a counter-example to any of the claims I have made about the work, nor have I ever seen it fail to provide help or relief to anyone who has tried it on its own terms.

This claim is something that may, at first, require genuine trust on your part to believe, but I would rather that you find out how true it is for yourselves. Just as I have made the invitation to you to join me in my search, there is also an invitation for you to show me where I am wrong. I am delighted to find where I am wrong because it is through finding out about our mistakes that we will all learn.

You see, I can't be hurt by making mistakes. I have made them before. I will make them again. The worst I – or any of us – can be at any given time, is wrong.[124]

The best I can be requires genuine trust.

In the first place, I must have a genuine trust in what Alexander wrote and what my teachers have demonstrated throughout the years. Secondly, I must have a genuine trust in myself that I will follow these procedures and do the work required to gain the skills and disciplines I need to learn this work. Thirdly, I must have a genuine trust that the manner in which I perform my activities and the way in which I behave is at least as important as what I do. But, most impor-tantly, I must trust in subjecting the processes directing my use to the experience of being dominated by reasoning instead of by feeling. I must trust in any proce-dure that I have reasoned out as best for my purpose even when the procedure might feel wrong or make me feel that I am wrong when I use it. I must trust in my reasoning processes to bring me safely to my dreams.

---

[124] If I have succeeded in my argument, this statement ought to seem more like a consolation than a threat.

THE RULES
OF THE GAME

Chapter 15

THE RULES OF THE GAME

YEARS AGO, in Cincinnati's version of Coney Island, my quest for the rules of success was begun. Because of a general phobia about the feelings associated with rapid acceleration, I was never a great fan of the rides at any amusement park. I liked being there, though, because I always enjoyed being around so many people who were having so much fun.

And there were the games.

I loved playing the games. I loved watching the games. I loved the challenge of trying to win even though the set up of the games made playing them a sucker's bet. I loved the challenge when I played. I loved the excitement when I won.

There was one game in particular which was my favorite.

It was called "Pokerino" and it consisted of a relatively short, downward-sloping inclined ramp, five hollow, rubber balls, and a flat area at the end of the ramp in which twenty-five holes were drilled. Inside each hole was an electronic trigger which, when depressed by a ball passing through, would light up a specific light on the backboard corresponding to a particular card from a poker deck, e.g. Ace of Hearts, King of Clubs, etc.

The object of the game was to roll the five balls down the ramp and light up the cards on the backboard. After the balls had been rolled and the "cards" determined, you would make the best poker hand possible out of the result. Because dropping a ball through the same hole could only light up a card once, it was possible to have less than five cards in your "hand" even after you had rolled five balls. I remember being "consistent" enough to have only one or two cards in my hand on many occasions.

Various numbers of coupons were awarded depending on the value of the poker hand made up of your lighted cards. Two Pairs was the lowest "hand" which won and yielded the smallest number of coupons and a Royal Flush (ten through ace in a single suit) was the highest winner with a payoff that seemed phenomenal. The coupons, in turn, could be redeemed for prizes like Teddy Bears and such. I really didn't care about the prizes, but, because I knew about Poker and because I knew about rolling balls down a ramp, "Pokerino" was a game that I thought I could learn to play well.

At first when I played, it seemed like I didn't win enough.

Oh, sometimes something would go wrong and I'd win. Usually just enough to keep me playing until my money ran out. But, as time went on, I became aware that I hardly won at all.

Just about the time this knowledge was beginning to seep in, I started to pay more attention to the barker, the man who would call out to people as they went by, trying to entice them to play.

Here I was guarding my chances, hoarding my quarters, putting every bit of concentration I could muster into how I would play each ball in each game, and I hardly ever won. There he was calling out to passers-by, engaging their curiosity in conversation, rolling the balls casually down the ramp, almost not paying attention, and he always won.

I don't mean he often won. I don't mean he usually won. I mean he always won.

Because I went to the park so seldom in any summer, it took many years to establish any kind of a relationship with this man. After about five years, he started to remember me and we became friends of a sort.

And all this time, through all of the demonstrations and all of his barking, he always won.

During this same time, I got a little better. I was able to win a little more – but he always won.

I never saw him lose.

Finally my curiosity overcame my shyness and I asked him how he could do it. I asked him how he won every time. I asked him how I could learn to never lose.

After I had asked him, he smiled a little and told me that it was partly because he played every day and I could only play now and again. I thanked him for his kindness and said that I was sure that practice helped, but he had said that that was only part of the answer and that I wanted to learn it all. When he saw that I was serious, and after he had looked around to make sure that one of his assistants had taken over, he proceeded to give me a lesson I have never forgotten.

For the next couple of hours he described to me the set up of the ramp, the way the ball speeds into the landing area, and the subtle bumps that had been placed in the "flat" landing area. He taught me how to use backspin while banking the ball off the sideboards of the ramp so that I could control the speed of the ball and increase the probability of the ball entering the landing area where I wanted it to be. He showed me how the card groupings in the landing area could be bunched together, in your mind, in various ways, to form larger target regions so that, each time you threw the ball, you could aim for a target area that would yield a good result from more than just one hole. He taught me all of the tricks and all of the skills required to play the game at a level of physical command.

Then he looked me in the eye and asked me if I understood all of that.

When I said, "Yes," he gave me the five balls and told me to show him.

As I played with his help and his correction, my level of play elevated again and again. He would ask me to make different shots – from the routine to the difficult. I began to win with an increasing regularity. After a while I became confident that I could make any shot that he asked for.

At that point he looked me in the eye again and asked me if I understood what he had told me and if I could do what I wanted to with the ball. When I assured him that I could, he said, "Fine. It's important to have that knowledge and those skills, but it will be next to meaningless if you can't learn what I'm about to tell you now.

"You asked me to tell you the secret of how I won all the time.

"Until you had become a good player, it would have done as much good to tell you as to refuse. Now that you can play well, I will tell you the secret, and maybe now, you'll be able to listen.

"When I get ready to play a game, I decide what the best score is that I could possibly get.

"In this game, it's a Royal Flush.

"I look at the board. I see where the ball has to go to give me the best chance of getting what I want. I decide how I have to shoot the ball to make it go there. I keep my goal in my mind; I make my shot as best as I can, and I accept what happens.

"Then, I look at where the ball goes, and what that means to my goal.

"If the chances for my goal are still there, I continue. If I have to change my goal, I change it and select a new region in the landing area to aim for. I decide how I have to shoot the ball to make it go where I will have the best chance to reach my goal. I keep my goal in my mind; I make my shot as best as I can, and I accept what happens.

"Then, I look at where the ball goes, and what that means to my goal.

"If the chances for my goal are still there, I continue. If I don't get what I want, I decide what the best possible goal is now. I decide where I want the ball to go to make the best goal happen, and how I have to shoot the ball to make it go there. I keep my goal in my mind; I make the best shot I can, and I accept what happens.

"Then, I look to see where the ball has gone.

"I see what it has done to my plans. If I can still get what I want, I go on with my original plan. If I can't get it anymore, I figure out the best results I can get with the shots that I have left. I decide where I want the ball to go to give me my best chance to get my best result. I decide how I have to shoot the ball to make it go there. I keep my goal in mind; I make the best shot I can, and I accept what happens.

"Then, I only have one ball left.

"But that makes things easy, because now the best goal I can reach should be pretty clear as well. I decide where the ball has to go to reach my goal. I decide how I have to shoot it to get it there. I keep my goal in mind, I make my best shot, and I accept what happens.

"And that's the secret to this game, son, and any other game you may play.

"Know what you want. Decide how to get it. Learn how to do the things you have to do to get your goal. Do those things as well as you can. Keep your goal in mind; take your best shot, and accept what happens. If you have to change, change; but, keep your goal in mind; take your best shot, and accept what happens.

"Something good will always come to you if you follow these rules."

With that he smiled and walked away.

There was nothing more to say.

I couldn't have said anything anyway, even if there had been something more to say. For, while he made this explanation and carried out his plan, I sat in silence and watched him roll, on demand, a perfect Royal Flush, the most difficult score to obtain.

*   *   *   *   *

Alexander gave us rules no less certain and no less precise. He showed us how to direct ourselves in a new and exciting way. He left a record for all to follow of the procedures he went through and of the skills we have to gain. Then, he urged us on to join him.

He taught us how to think, and he shared with us the pitfalls we will all face as we seek to elevate our own standard levels of general use. Alexander believed that the next "great phase in man's advancement [will be] that in which he passes from subconscious to conscious control of his own mind and body."[125] He believed that by disciplining the power of our conscious, reasoning minds, we can learn to reach beyond our present state, and begin to make real the dreams we hold within.

He warned us that there will be trials and setbacks and frustrations and confusions along the way, but he assured us that we can do at least as well as he, if we will only do what he did. We can't do just part of it, though. We must do and learn and grow through it all.

We must understand the rules. We must see what needs to be done. We must learn the skills required to accomplish these goals, and then put them into practice. We must learn to watch and assess our results and our procedures, not as an immediate form of guidance or judgment, but merely as a part of the conditions present. We must learn to carry on in ways we have reasoned out as best for our purpose until changing becomes unavoidable. And always, we must learn to trust that our reasoning processes will bring us all safely to all of our chosen ends.

---

[125] Jones, Frank Pierce, *Freedom to Change.* Mouritz, London, 1997, p. 24.

APPENDICES

Appendix A

FOR A DARN GOOD REASON[126]

OVER THE YEARS, much has been said about the innovations that Marjorie Barstow has brought to her teaching of the movement discoveries of F.M. Alexander. People have both praised and vilified these procedures depending upon the fixed ideas that they brought to their process of appraisal.

More recently, the advent of the NASTAT organization (now AmSTAT) has fostered a political uproar throughout the profession in the United States. This has led to a characterization of various teaching methods as being either "traditional" or "non-traditional." While such labels may be good public relations on the part of the so-called "traditionalists," the labels themselves can be misleading if not intentionally deceptive. "Traditional" in what sense? According to what standards? From which of the many possible starting points does the "tradition" begin?

More importantly, the use of these terms to shape our perceptions about the work, and the methods by which they are communicated to others, prevents us from seeing the true nature of the transactions involved in the work and in teaching it. By taking a closer look at the history of teaching and teacher training, and at the nature of the transactions involved in learning this work, this paper will seek to place Ms. Barstow's innovations in a more appropriate context than is implied by the label "non-traditional," and to reveal the common task which we as teachers all face: a task that provides a more appropriate target for our energies than squabbling with one another.

The use of the term "traditional," in these arguments, creates a myth and a blindspot.

The term "traditional" is being used now to indicate the relative adherence to a certain pattern of teaching and training that has been used in England and the United States for much of the last thirty years or more. In this view, there is a

---

[126] This article was written in 1988 as part of another project. In spite of the wholesale changes in the body of this book, for many reasons I decided that it would be important to leave this article pretty much as it was and it is included here with only just a few changes from the original. In addition to changes in tense to acknowledge that Marjorie passed away during the interval between editions, the only other changes that have been made have been for the purpose of correction, clarification, and the inclusion of supporting material that was not available at the time this piece was first written. Almost everything else – including the writing style, use of language, tone, and opinions – remain just as they were.

model for teaching the work that underlies these patterns as well as certain procedures for teaching and training that fit the model.

The impression made by the use of the term "traditional" is that this particular manner of teaching stretches back to Mr. Alexander. The word "traditional" implies that Alexander's procedures have been brought forward, through time, intact. As a result, the argument goes, work done in this way is somehow pure and untainted by experiment. There is an implication that only "traditional" work is of benefit, and that most or all "non-traditional" work is so different and inferior that it should even be called by a different name.

As we shall see, this implication is insupportable by the facts that we have. To continue to hold this view requires either a selective memory about the history of the work, or the improbable assumption that a work that deals with change would itself remain unchanged. Most importantly, it misapprehends the basic nature of the work as well as Mr. Alexander's part in it. It establishes concepts about the work that are contrary to fact and counter-productive as a basis for teaching or learning the work.

To avoid the errors inherent in these presumed and fictitious virtues of "traditional" training and teaching, it will be necessary to take a fresh look at our origins in the work once again.

*   *   *   *   *

First of all, one does not need a teacher to learn the Alexander Technique.[127] It seems obvious, but I am always surprised by how many people fail to realize or

---

[127] The term "Alexander Technique" is used here to mean the broad spectrum of activities and behaviors suggested, altered, or implied by the movement discoveries of F.M. Alexander. In his lifetime, Alexander never gave a name to the set of principles that he articulated, or to the processes used to communicate these ideas. In fact, many authors inform us that he took great pains to avoid doing so. "How can you name anything which is so comprehensive?" he once wrote in a letter. It seems his preference was to refer to the whole of what he thought or did as "the work." 'The name "Alexander Technique" came to be applied only after his death.

I have heard it argued that the "Alexander Technique" should be defined more narrowly. The argument states that the term should be used only to describe the teaching of Mr. Alexander's principles in a certain way, i.e., in the "way that Mr. Alexander taught them." As we shall see in this paper, that concept is problematic because it is highly improbable that anyone teaches "that way" anymore, nor did Alexander, if the course of his whole career as a teacher is compared to itself. The major issue involved between opting for the restricted use of the term as opposed to the broader sense is that we must decide whether we are trying to trademark a particular set of protocols for teaching and employing Mr. Alexander's "work," OR whether we are trying to identify a group of principles, discoveries, and ideas whose applications are as flexible as the ideas themselves. For the reasons

consider that Alexander taught himself. If the acquisition of this knowledge and the capacity to use it was based upon receiving "correct sensory experience from a properly trained teacher," then the whole process would never have been started. The very fact of Alexander's personal success eliminates from consideration the contention that a "properly trained teacher" is required to learn this work.

Alexander learned this work, and Alexander had only himself.

Actually, he had two other things as well.

In the beginning, Alexander started with a problem and an idea. The problem is well known: his faulty breathing and his throat trouble. So is his idea: that his difficulties were due to something which he did to himself in his *manner* of performance. This idea was based on the observation that he lost his voice in performance, but not in ordinary speaking. From this observation, he postulated that there was some procedure, or set of procedures, which he did differently while reciting, which he did not do in ordinary speaking, and which caused his problem. Having come to this conclusion, he then devised an experiment to test his idea.

As he carried out his experiments, he gathered information about the procedures that he did use in speaking and reciting. After a long period of experimentation, he evaluated his results. On the basis of the results of his experiments, he was forced to revise his ideas about the source of his difficulties.

His original idea was wrong in one way. There was not some actual procedure that he did differently while reciting; he had the same three tendencies of disruptive movement in both speaking and reciting. Yet, in another way, his original idea – that there was something different about his manner of speaking and reciting – was right. While the actual procedures were the same in both speaking and reciting, he observed that there was a marked difference in the degree of effort with which these procedures were performed in the two activities. Even when his ideas were wrong, because he followed a five-part process of observation, postulation, experimentation, evaluation, and adaptation, he was still able to derive benefit.

He then took his new observation about this difference of degree, formulated another idea about its importance ("that these three tendencies (constituted) a misuse of the parts concerned"), performed further experimentation, and, after evaluating the results, adapted his ideas once more. He followed this procedure of observation, experimentation, and refinement again and again and again and again, even after he had already achieved a high degree of success in solving his

---

given in this article, this broader sense of the term "Alexander Technique" will he used and meant throughout this paper.

original problem.[128] He followed this procedure until, to his satisfaction, he had gotten to the root of the solution for improving the use of himself.

Alexander taught himself. He taught himself by using the same process of investigation he used to make his discoveries. It is clear that this process of investigation is a necessary part of the foundation of his lifework. When Alexander tells us that we can do what he does if we will do what he did, he means this process of investigation just as surely as he means "let the neck be free in order to let the head go forward and up in order to let the back broaden and lengthen."

Alexander taught himself through this detailed process. With it, he discovered increasingly clearer understandings of how to improve his own self-use. In so doing, he represents the first generation of both Alexander teachers and students.

      *   *   *   *   *

The next generation of students is represented by Alexander's first students in Australia.

Other people had noticed the benefits that Alexander had gained for himself from his work. They asked him to teach them what he had learned. Here, Alexander's task appeared to be different. Rather than teaching himself by following his own procedures to make new discoveries, his new problem seemed to be how he could communicate what he had learned to others. As before, he began with what he knew.

With respect to the work, Alexander had ideas. He had information of value that would benefit his students if only he could communicate his experiences and understandings to them. But, just as he had no one to teach him the work, he had no one to train him as a teacher of others. So, while we have no certain knowledge of the procedures he used, the most consistent and probable course of action for him to follow was to solve his new problem in the very same way that he had set out to make his initial discoveries.[129]

He started with his ideas. He decided what each idea meant and how it could best be communicated. He made up protocols to implement his ideas to see how well they worked. He evaluated his results. When his procedures worked, he

---

[128] "With the prevention of the misuse of these parts I tended to become less hoarse while reciting, and that as I gradually gained experience in this prevention, my liability to hoarseness tended to decrease," lines 216-220 on page 28 from "The Evolution of a Technique" in Alexander's third book, *The Use of the Self*, the Gollancz edition. The entire chapter, as printed in this edition, is 889 lines in length.

[129] As we shall see, later examples about how to teach, for which we have some documentation, follow this outline, and therefore support this hypothesis.

kept them. When his ideas and procedures were proven to be of less value through his experimentation, he changed them.

In other words, when Alexander made a decision about how to teach, he acted upon his best knowledge and understanding, as his experience informed him, at every given moment. When he had an idea, he tested it. If his idea proved unsound (and he had many which did), he set the idea aside or tested it further. If it proved of value, he brought the idea and the procedures derived from the idea into his work, and tested it further.

He always proceeded from an idea. He always tested further. As a result, his process of learning how to teach was not only just as evolutionary as his original process of discovery, but it followed the same process of investigation.

It is important that we see Alexander's work as changeable and changing.

If we lock ourselves into some fantasy that the work is a monolithic, complete, and finished whole, then we will have denied ourselves its essence. One of the hidden pitfalls in our tendencies to preserve any particular protocol is that it gives the impression that we have reached some endpoint in the evolution of teaching methods. In the teaching of a process of improvement, this seems unlikely.

In making his early discoveries, Alexander's ideas were tested. In making his last discoveries, Alexander's ideas were tested. When these tests demonstrated the need, his ideas about the work, and about how to teach it, changed. By looking at some of the early major changes in Alexander's teaching methods, we can see this principle of constant investigation, constant evaluation, and constant change at work.

*   *   *   *   *

For instance, take the issue of the use of hands in teaching. Maisel tells us in his introduction to *The Resurrection of the Body* about Alexander's early work in London. Maisel claims that both Alexander brothers taught by verbal instruction alone.[130] He characterizes the two brothers as being at opposite ends of the studio "shouting their disparate and desperate instructions at (their) victims."[131]

In addition, Maisel gives us the impression that this process was unsatisfactory: "Initially Alexander had attempted – in words, futile words – to teach the new feeling by *telling* his pupils how to attain it."[132] The problem with this characterization is that, had teaching with minimal manipulation been that useless, one would be hard pressed to account for Alexander's being in London. He was there because of the success of his teaching method in Australia. How can one account for the success of Alexander in Australia if teaching in this way was as futile as Maisel would have us believe?

If we accept Maisel's account (if only to some degree), it is clear that teaching with minimal use of one's hands was possible because the Alexander brothers had success with it. As a result, we have proof, once more, that one does not need proper kinesthetic experience to be imparted by a properly trained teacher in order to learn this work.[133]

Frank Jones' book contains a different and provocative reflection on Alexander and his methods with respect to the use of his hands in teaching:

F.M. told me that in 1914 he was just beginning to find a new way of using his hands in teaching. By applying the inhibitory control (which had proved so effective in breathing and speaking) to the use of his hands, he was learning to

---

[130] Walter Carrington disputes the possibility of teaching without the use of hands in his printed discussions with Seán Carey (*Walter Carrington on the Alexander Technique*, Sheildrake Press, London, 1986, p. 10). Perhaps the telling point in this issue is not whether there was teaching without hands, but rather the degree or amount of manipulation used. It might even be that, at this time, there was only a minimum amount of manipulation. Whatever the case, this account will proceed on the assumption that there was sufficient evidence to support a high degree of accuracy in Maisel's reportage. As we shall see, a strict accuracy is not necessary to the main argument presented.

[131] Maisel, Edward, *The Resurrection of the Body. S*hambala Publications, Inc., Boston, MA, p. xxvii.

[132] *ibid.*, p. xxvii.

[133] It has been suggested by some that this is merely evidence in favor of this contention that teaching can be successful without proper kinesthetic information being imparted rather than a proof. According to Maisel's information, there was successful teaching with minimal or no manipulation. Because proper kinesthetic experience can only be an after-effect of manipulation, if there was successful teaching without manipulation, then there was successful teaching without proper kinesthetic experience being imparted. If there was successful teaching without proper kinesthetic experience being imparted, then it can be done, and, therefore, proper kinesthetic experience imparted by a properly trained teacher is not necessary to learn the work. To me, that is a proof.

make changes in a pupil that were different from ordinary manipulation or postural adjustment.[134]

Some take this to be a confirmation of the "hand-less" teaching that had gone before, and suggest that this means that, before 1914, Alexander did not use his hands. It seems more likely to me that he was using his hands to make adjustments in lessons before this time, but, in 1914, he began to apply his own principles to the *manner* in which he used his hands. Regardless of which characterization is true, this is very exciting information on two counts.

First of all, Alexander is reported as saying that he was *beginning* to use his hands in this way. Alexander did not characterize this change as that he "began," or that he had changed strategies with a bolt of insight and certainty, but that he was "beginning to find a new way of using his hands," as one would begin any experimental practice. In 1914, this application of the inhibitory control to the use of his hands in teaching represented the latest change in Alexander's continuing effort to find the optimum way to communicate the work.

The second point of excitement is that, with this information, we are faced with the certainty that there was successful teaching without the employment of any inhibitory control in the use of the teacher's hands.

By 1914, Alexander had been in London for ten years. He had not only had a successful teaching practice, but, by this time, he had published his first two books.[135] During these ten years, Alexander was enjoying great success without inhibition as a controlling factor in the use of his hands. But, in spite of his success, in 1914, he began using his hands in a new and different way. Why? Because he thought of it; it was consistent with his principles and ideas; and upon experimentation, he found that it worked better than the procedures he was using before.

There can be no clearer proof of Alexander's constant efforts at improvement and change in his manner of teaching.

The need to keep applying these principles of improvement and change to his own manner of teaching and exploration of the work itself was so great that, in spite of his success as a teacher, Alexander continued to submit his work to the very process he used to make his initial discoveries. In spite of his success, he was unwilling to assume that he had reached an endpoint in exploring or teach-

---

[134] Jones, Frank Pierce, *Freedom to Change*. Mouritz, London, 1997, p. 31.

[135] The 140-page version of *Man's Supreme Inheritance* published in 1910 and *Conscious Control* published in 1912. The two books were combined for the 1918 version published by Dutton with further additions. This combined version has come to be the standard version.

ing his work.[136] As we see these constant changes in his work, it is important to remember that the process that he used to discover and refine these teaching procedures was the same process of investigation that he used initially to make his discoveries.

*   *   *   *   *

Each time Alexander made a major change in what he was doing he initiated a change in the "generation" of student involved.

His trip to London was, in large part, a change in generation brought about by bringing the work to a larger and more sophisticated audience. Therefore, his interaction with his early students in London can be seen as a "third generation" of Alexander students. It is the nature of the next two generations of students, however, which is the most interesting.

Students who were given instructions that included more liberal usage of the teacher's hands, instead of primarily verbal instruction, were different from the students who had come before. The use of hands as a primary tool in teaching represents the institution of a new idea and a new strategy for teaching. It represents an attempt to bring the student more directly into the process of learning by engaging him more fully from the outset. The use of hands in teaching was kept, in addition to verbal instruction, because, on testing, it proved valuable.

Those students who began their study (or continued their study with an open and flexible mind) after the change in 1914 were fundamentally different from even students who had been taught with hands before. People who have experienced what it is like to be taught by someone who is not using inhibitory controls in their hands can easily appreciate this distinction. Without the use of inhibitory controls, the teacher's hands feel different. Without these controls, the quality and clarity of the information conveyed is dramatically reduced. The introduction of these inhibitory controls by the teacher in the use of his hands in teaching is a major change in the technology of teaching that created yet another generation of students of the work.

Those of us who have had the privilege of studying with Marjorie Barstow for a long time have seen this process of creating generations of students at work. With each new major innovation, with each new major insight, with each improvement in the process of communicating the work effectively, a new

---

[136] It is interesting to note that Carrington does not dispute this process of constant change (*Walter Carrington on the Alexander Technique,* Sheildrake Press, London, 1986, p. 18), although he chooses to characterize the nature of the changes as being subtle. One wonders if that over time the accretion of many subtle changes did not amount to at least a few substantial ones.

generation of students is created in Nebraska among the students who are beginning their study.

Students who started in Nebraska after the 1985 summer workshop find it hard to believe that we used to stay in one large group in one hot room for four consecutive hours. Students who started in the late '70's find it hard to believe that Marjorie once used "heavy hands" more than "light hands."[137] People who started in the mid '70's find it hard to believe that "doing activities" was not always a priority. Almost everyone who works with Marjorie now finds it hard to believe that we used to get in and out of chairs regularly, that Marjorie would never teach wearing anything but a dress or skirt, or that she would almost never joke or kid around while teaching.

Each change in her work began as an idea. Each idea became an experiment. When experimentation proved the change valuable, it was kept.

But, each new student who comes to Nebraska believes that the procedures, methods, and terminology employed when he began his study was the best way to teach and THE WAY that teaching was always done before his arrival. Each succeeding generation of students in Nebraska believes that the procedures in place when they began their study represented a long-standing tradition of teaching that had always happened in just that way. With some of these students it is difficult to persuade them to continue to adapt to Marjorie's new discoveries and methods. In fact, some hold on to their initial understandings and impressions so tightly that accurate predictions about when they began to study with Marjorie can be made by identifying the era during which their fixed ideas about the work were first being articulated.

---

[137] It has been pointed out to me recently (in 2003) that these terms "light hands" and "heavy hands" are confusing to people who were not present in Nebraska during the times the active investigation between the two different approaches to teaching was taking place. As a result, I realized that these two titles do not convey their complete meaning when seen in isolation like this. While there was a clear difference between the relative "weight" or pressure applied in the two different approaches and while there is general agreement that a lighter touch is more effective in teaching (often this claim is made in reference to the superior nature of lessons given by both Alexander brothers after they recovered from their strokes), the real telling difference between the two had more to do with the role of the teacher in the learning experience.

"Heavy hands" was the approach to teaching in which almost everything was done for the student. In this approach, the experience given to the student was a complete process that provided information for the student to sort out afterwards. In the "light hands" approach, very little manual input was used. The intent was to give the student a suggestion or a fragment of the whole experience in order to encourage the student to make the necessary leap to the whole of the experience on his or her own. This was believed to be a process that would promote the student's self-reliance and powers of originality while diminishing the student's dependence on the teacher or seeing the teacher as the main source of "right" answers.

The present procedures being used by Marjorie at any given time do not represent some unyielding "tradition," but rather the best application of her current thinking about the work and how to teach it. This has always been true of Marjorie's teaching.[138] As we have seen, it was also true of Mr. Alexander and his work.

There never was ONE RIGHT WAY to teach the work. There was only a teacher faced with the task of how to communicate the work most effectively and the five-part process of investigation which Alexander continually used – observation, postulation, experimentation, evaluation, and adaptation – applied to the process of learning to teach the work.

*   *   *   *   *

The same kinds of changes and the same process of investigation can be seen when one looks at the history of teacher training.

As we noted above, Alexander was required to train himself to teach.

As with learning the work, Alexander's personal success in training himself to teach is testimony that instruction in how to teach from a properly trained teacher is not required to become a successful teacher. This is not to say that the efforts to establish genuine standards and practices to improve all training programs is not important. I merely wish to point out that blanket statements about the necessity of any particular kind of training program to become a teacher of this work are simply not true, and that there is no greater counter-example than Mr. Alexander himself.[139]

---

[138] Although I had only worked with Marjorie since 1971 when I wrote this, Frank Jones affirmed this perception from his work with her in the forties when she worked as A.R.'s assistant in Boston. Others, whom I have met in Lincoln and elsewhere, have also affirmed this about her since her return from the first teacher-training course.

[139] Some may argue that it requires a special and nearly unique individual like Alexander to become a teacher without "proper" training, but this is not true. If there is any good news in this work, it is that anyone who will follow the principles that Alexander discovered and use the process of investigation he developed can learn the work. Anyone who then applies this knowledge and process of investigation to the problem of communicating the work to others can learn to teach it. The undeniable advantage of a training program is a compression of the time required to achieve a significant level of proficiency through the guidance of instructors, as well as the wealth of knowledge gained by interaction within a like-minded community. Still, a training program is not required for someone to become a teacher. All that is required to become a teacher is an understanding of the work and of how to communicate it effectively to others. Both of these understandings must be based on an appropriate process of investigation. Only a training program that accomplishes these things would be of value. But, by the same token, all training programs that accomplish these things would be of value, regardless of their structure.

Alexander's process of discovering how to communicate his work to others most effectively was never ending. Neither were his efforts to learn how to train teachers.

When demand for the work grew, Alexander recruited his brother, A.R. (Albert Redden), to join him. Certainly A.R. was not the beneficiary of an extended training program. He was trained in Australia during the time that little, if any, work was done by hand. He received primarily verbal instructions in the principles and concepts. His training could best be described as a brief apprenticeship, since he claimed to have needed only six lessons to learn the work,[140] and he later boasted that he never required the use of hands to learn the work. Yet, A.R. seems to have been the teacher in whom F.M. showed the greatest confidence.

As such, A.R. represents the second generation of teachers and the first teacher trained by apprenticeship.

We do not know, specifically, how Ethel Webb, Margaret Goldie, and Irene Tasker were trained. Information about this process is sparse.[141] We do know that, by the time the first teacher-training course was held, these three women were already trained and working as assistants to the Alexander brothers in both secretarial and teaching capacities.

What is most probably true is that they, too, experienced an apprenticeship with the two brothers in which their own manner of use was improved through lessons and personal application while the mechanics of teaching and the process of investigation was communicated to each commensurate with her capacity and as circumstances required.

I have never heard a disparaging remark about the quality of these women as teachers. In her article about the first training course in "The Alexander Review," Erika Whittaker's comments about Ethel Webb and Irene Tasker, with respect to their training and quality, is typical: "Neither of them had 'trained,' but what wonderful teachers they were!"

About the worst that I have ever heard said about them were comments about the greater expertise of the Alexander brothers. This should not be a surprise to anyone, nor should it really be construed as a criticism of their work. Only rarely does the work of apprentices or journeymen exceed that of their masters. And, even then, it is far rarer for this ascendancy to occur while the newer adept remains closely associated with the master, particularly when the master continues in a process of improvement and discovery as Alexander did.

---

[140] In conversation, Marjorie Barstow has said it may have taken even fewer lessons than that.

[141] Walter Carrington tells us that, when Ethel Webb asked Mr. Alexander for advice on how to teach, he told her, "Just don't do anything you have ever seen me do." Ms. Webb was often fond of saying that this advice "was my training."

Still, we are faced with the fact that before the first teacher-training course began, Alexander had already trained two separate generations of teachers, in addition to himself, by apprenticeship.

Even if we consider the backgrounds of the founders of the teacher-training program in New York, we find that "neither Judith (Leibowitz] nor Debbie [Caplan] had been formally trained, as it were, but both had learned a great deal over the years"[142] before they founded their training program.

Clearly, the oldest and longest-standing "tradition" in training teachers in this work is brief or extended apprenticeships.

*   *   *   *   *

Once we get to the first teacher-training course, we come face to face with the original model on which so-called "traditional" teaching and training is allegedly based. Once again we are faced with the problem of controversy because there is no formal, reliable, contemporary history of the man and his time. Increasingly, recollections are being shared with us by the principals who survived Alexander, but there is so much disagreement that the reliability of these recollections must be questioned.[143]

For instance, Maisel places Alexander's last encounter with the doctor prior to the start of his investigation in the year 1888.[144] Lulie Westfeldt says that Alexander had been a successful recitationist for years when he began to have

---

[142] Carrington, Walter, with Carey, Seán, *Walter Carrington on the Alexander Technique,* Sheildrake Press, London, 1986, p. 25. Carrington goes on to point out that not only could people who were not "formally trained" he good teachers, but they could also be effective trainers of teachers. Leibowitz and Caplan, he tells us, "set up a two-year training course and, although it suffered from a number of inadequacies and shortcomings, some of the people who went through the training have gone on to become established and competent teachers – Frank Ottiwell who lives in San Francisco is a good example."

It is clear from this that it is not necessary to be "formally trained" in any particular way to be either a teacher or a trainer of teachers.

[143] In her article in "The Alexander Review," Erika Whittaker says, "If all seven of us first ones in that course were to recount our individual memories there would be quite a diversity of stories – and it must be admitted that we tend to only remember what we want to remember!" (p. 22)

[144] Maisel, Edward, *The Resurrection of the Body.* Shambala Press, Boston & London, 1969, p. xii.

trouble in 1892.[145] Frank Jones does not give a specific date for any specific occurrence but places the events in the early 1890's.[146]

Similarly, at the First International Congress, Marjory Barlow and Marjorie Barstow were in direct disagreement about the presence and use of a table for lying-down work done by Alexander at the time of the first teacher-training program. (Erika Whittaker seems to agree with Mrs. Barlow about the presence of the furniture, at least, by remembering a kind of trestle table in the small back room.) If we cannot reach agreement about such seemingly simple, once verifiable, phenomena as the furniture, small wonder that our attempts to reach agreement about the subtle, substantive nuances of complex ideas and meanings in the work have proved futile!

When looking at the recollections of the first teacher-training course, we are presented with varying views of the experience. These views range from satisfaction to strong criticism.

Erika Whittaker's article, although brief, provides a look at the time that is nostalgic and caring. It contains many interesting remembrances about the course and the people in it. It communicates a spirit of adventure and self-reliance that must have been a common characteristic among these pioneering students. While she points out some of the shortcomings of the course's planning and the personalities involved, she herself seemed quite capable of changing to meet these challenges and of obtaining value from the experience.

Mrs. Whittaker's response to the informality of the program approaches delight. "I think the very fact that there were no rules and regulations encouraged us to make use of the time together [on their own and away from direct instruction with Alexander] in a much less restricted way."[147]

She talks of how the students worked together to learn new things even if it meant doing crazy things. "We considered observation, inhibition, direction – we devised various ways of observing each other in a variety of activities.... . With non-endgaining and working out means whereby, we had a most interesting time exploring new ways of doing familiar things."[148]

In other words, the manner of her procedure – starting with principle and observation, devising experiments to explore the meanings of these principles, and

---

[145] Westfeldt, Lulie, F. Matthias *Alexander: the Man and his Work.* Centerline Press, Los Angeles, 1965, p. 125.

[146] Jones, op. cit., p. 16.

[147] Whittaker, Erika, "England – The First Training Course." *The Alexander Review*, Vol. 2, No. 3. Centerline Press, Los Angeles, 1987, p. 23.

[148] *ibid.*, p. 23.

evaluating the results obtained – fits the model of Alexander's process of investigation, and led her to a very satisfying result.

The most vocal critic of the first teacher-training course is Lulie Westfeldt in her book, F. *Matthias Alexander: the Man and his Work.*

In particular, her assessment of the course and of the progress of the students in the third year was very critical. "We began to suspect that we were on our own. We would have to hold ourselves responsible for learning his work as best we could. Alexander was there, and we might in some way learn how to get what we needed from him, or we might not. We could not count on him for anything."[149]

Although her tone of disappointment is quite clear, her acknowledgement of the student's responsibility for learning the work seems to be consistent with Alexander's views on the subject. In spite of this acknowledgement, and because of the failings she saw in the training course and in their instructor, she later claims that the course was so bad that "if we had left at the end of our third year, we could not possibly have survived as teachers."[150]

Miss Westfeldt then tells us that, in her opinion, two unexpected happenings saved the first training course.

First of all, a fourth year was added. This presumably gave the remaining students time to overcome the deficits of their first three years of training.

The second unexpected event was when an unnamed colleague[151] pointed out that they had all missed the boat. He had a low opinion of what they all knew

---

[149] Westfeldt, op. cit., pp. 62-63.

[150] *ibid.*, p. 85. It is also interesting to note that Miss Westfeldt also claims that all of the training course members stayed. This is simply not the case. Marjorie Barstow left after the initial three-year period. In light of this fact, it is not surprising that Ms. Barstow is one of the people who has expressed great satisfaction about the first training course in its original form.

[151] Almost all of the principals in Miss Westfeldt's book are unnamed. This is a great disappointment and a constant source of frustration in trying to find through-lines in the thoughts of individuals in the work. Reading Carrington's discussions with Seán Carey, (*Walter Carrington on the Alexander Technique,* Sheildrake Press, London, 1986, p. 11) one is given the impression that this unnamed colleague may have been Patrick Macdonald, but there is no clear proof in print of which I am aware. This contention, however, was later confirmed at tea during the Brighton Congress by Erika Whittaker, Marjorie Barstow, and Sir George Trevelyan. (It has recently come to my attention that in Shoshana Kaminitz's obituary for Patrick Macdonald, she also makes the claim that the unnamed colleague was Patrick Macdonald. Although she supplies no direct evidence for this, she does include the handwritten inscription that Lulie made in the copy of the book she presented to him: "for my friend Patrick Macdonald who pulled the first Training Course out of the mire and thereby made possible all other training courses." [STAT News, spring 1992, p. 9] Another fact that is often overlooked in this connection is that

and what they could do as teachers. Because of perceived deficiencies in the training course, he said they would have to "somehow or other pull [themselves] up by their own bootstraps."[152]

The importance Miss Westfeldt placed on this colleague's contribution is evident. "Without (her colleague's) clear sensing of the problem and his creative thought in helping us solve it, we would have failed as teachers, fourth year or no."[153]

Miss Westfeldt's point is clear.

In her opinion, the most important factor in her becoming trained successfully as a teacher was not how long she had studied, or even that she had studied in Alexander's training program. The most important factor, according to her, was what her group did in response to making the observation that there was a problem to be solved. Her group solved this problem by taking independent action.

And what was the independent action that her group – away from the training course and on their own – took in response to the observation that Miss Westfeldt was to claim made the difference in the success of their training? "We worked as in a laboratory, using each other as guinea pigs, the group mind gradually bringing to light the problems involved."[154]

They carried out experiments! They evaluated their results! When the results warranted, they changed their ideas! As they carried out this procedure, "simultaneously our minds and our hands advanced in knowledge."[155]

In other words, by Miss Westfeldt's own account, as soon as the disgruntled members of her group in the training program applied themselves to the learning of the work in the same way that Alexander discovered it, "as in a laboratory," their knowledge advanced. As soon as they relied upon active experimentation with Alexander's principles and ideas, away from their teacher and on their own, rather than relying on being "taught" somehow by someone, they began to experience the same kind of growth in themselves and in their understanding of the work which Alexander had experienced himself.

---

when Patrick "saved" the training course from FM's shortcomings, he was only 25 years old.)

[152] *ibid.*, p. 86. It is interesting to see that although the emotional flavor of the colleague's opinion and Miss Westfeldt's differ from Mrs. Whittaker's, the placement of responsibility on the student for learning the work and the strategy they all employ to bring about constructive change is the same.

[153] *ibid.*, p. 86.

[154] *ibid.*, pp. 86-87.

[155] *ibid.*, p. 87.

It was the introduction of self-reliance within a more appropriate process of investigation that saved the course for even one of Alexander's harshest critics. As Miss Westfeldt said, "the factors making our success (as teachers) possible were the realistic appraisal of F.M., belief in and enthusiasm for his work, *creative resourcefulness,*[156] *ability to stand prolonged discipline*[157] and *ability to work together as a group with trust and cooperation.*"[158] The need for these same factors remains with us today.

*　　　*　　　*　　　*　　　*

When we look at the work done by the Master Teachers who founded training programs, we see that all of them have changed the work in some way.

Marjorie Barstow's many changes are the source of much discussion. Walter Carrington tells us of some of the changes which he made in the training course immediately after Alexander's death: the daily lecture, the regular private lessons, the institution of the afternoon "games" in which a specific procedure is worked on in groups of threes, and the early use of hands on other students as a non-endgaining activity. Similarly, Patrick Macdonald – whatever the true nature of his influence on the way in which teaching was done during the first teacher-training courses – has introduced his series of gymnastics into his work, e.g., the Lunge, the Yo-Yo and Elevator.

Why did these teachers break with the traditions and the manner in which they had been taught to introduce these new procedures into their teaching and training practices? Because these new procedures matched their models and ideas of what they thought the work was, and upon experimentation, these changes proved to be of value to their students.

As their ideas about (and understanding of) the work grew, their willingness to experiment and improve themselves and their work grew with it. As their ideas about (and understanding of) the work grows in the future, I am sure this new growth will be reflected in changes in their procedures.

In this way, it is important for all of us to see that the oldest tradition in this work is not any particular method of teaching or learning, but rather the active investigation of how to improve one's own self-use and how to improve one's own manner of teaching through observation, experimentation, and change.

Even as stalwart a preservationist as Marjory Barlow, Alexander's niece, is not immune to the pressures of improved understanding.

---

[156] All of these italics are mine.
[157] See Chapters 11-14.
[158] *ibid.*, p. 88.

At the First International Congress, Mrs. Barlow, with some delight, showed our group some new discoveries that she had made in the functioning of the foot in standing. She was quite proud and pleased to share it with us, though it was different from how she was taught, and not part of "traditional" teaching. She explained her deviation from standard cant and procedure by saying, "I teach everything exactly the way that my uncle did, except when I have a darn good reason to change."[159] As we have seen, her standard for making a change – having a darn good reason based on observation and experimentation – is consistent with the very nature of the work.

*   *   *   *   *

This work represents an on-going process of increasingly fine appreciation of Alexander's ideas that can be used to improve our lives in various ways.

I am constantly amused when I hear myself, or others, say, "Oh! I know what that is!" in a lesson. Each "new answer" which I discover seems, at that moment, like such a final solution. My experience has shown me, though, that my present "new answer" will sooner or later be replaced by another "new answer" which may sound, or even feel, remarkably like the old one.

The most common form this has taken in classes in Nebraska is for the student to say, "Oh! You mean that I should move my head and let my body follow! Why didn't you say that before!?!"

I do not object to this kind of complaint from one of my students. It demonstrates to me that some fundamental understanding in this work has reached some further degree of clarity in thought and action.

What I object to is when my students (or anyone else) take their new understanding and represent it as anything more than just a new understanding. We must eliminate this tendency to accept and propose that any present understanding that we may have is "IT." We must all learn to admit freely that while we may have learned a lot, experimented a lot, grown a lot, and changed a lot, we have not yet reached an endpoint for learning and changing and growth with respect to this work. In fact, if Mr. Alexander was right in what he said and believed about this work, we cannot reach such an endpoint.

The only way in which it makes any sense to preserve and adhere to any particular form of teaching, without testing it constantly, is to propose that the teachers performing this particular form of teaching have reached some endpoint in the work. But Alexander wrote in the "Introductory" to *The Universal Constant in Living* that "after working for a lifetime in this new field I am conscious

---

[159] Personal notebooks kept during lectures.

that the knowledge gained is but a beginning."[160] If, after fifty years of investigation, Alexander had just reached the beginnings of the work, it seems highly presumptuous for any of us to believe that in the last sixty years we have found the end.

In fact, there is a way in which picking the final endpoint of the Alexander Technique is like designating the exact moment "now" by shouting out the word when it occurs. No matter how often you shout, there is always a "now" to come. No matter how often one decides that one finally understands this work, there is another refinement to come.

In the more than twenty years that I knew Marjorie Barstow, I never failed to be struck by the amount of substantive change and improvement she made in her thinking, movement, and teaching during the time we had been apart.

Marjorie's manner of teaching did not spring forth in full bloom in its present form as an expression of personality or style. It was very much the product of a reasoned and conscious evolution. While it is true that much of what she did appeared to be casual, everything which she did (or didn't do) while teaching had been reasoned out and tested. It had been tried against the standards of Alexander's ideas. Ideas and procedures that were used in her teaching were kept because they accomplished something new, something better, or they accomplished the same thing more easily. Those ideas and procedures that were discarded were eliminated because they no longer seemed to be of value.

Every new procedure underwent preliminary evaluation and thought. The procedure was then tested. Each experiment was founded upon the ideas that underlay the new procedure. These ideas, and the results which their related procedures produced, were then tested again against Mr. Alexander's ideas and procedures.

This constant process of observation, postulation, experimentation, evaluation, and adaptation continued in every class and every lesson I ever saw Marjorie Barstow teach. No innovation was ever adopted without this stringent testing. No change was ever made without a darn good reason.

This universally constant effort on Marjorie's part to improve her general standard level of use and teaching by the application of Alexander's principles and his process of investigation is not only consistent with Alexander's work, it lies at the very heart of it. Any teacher who is truly following this process of investigation, and who is truly employing these principles cannot help but change and improve in both personal self-use and teaching methods. Any teacher whose manner or methods are constant and unchanging is, at best, suspect and, at worst, what that teacher is doing may be antithetical to the work.

---

[160] Alexander, F.M., *The Universal Constant in Living*. Mouritz, London, 2000, p. xxxvi.

On the other hand, merely to change one's teaching method for the sake of change is not an answer. Without using Alexander's process of investigation as a basis, this kind of arbitrary change would also be contrary to the work.

No, the answer lies in the solution suggested by Marjory Barlow. One should stay with what one knows as one continues to experiment and consider. Finally, when one has developed a darn good reason to change, one should change.

We need to see that there is no difference between applying Alexander's process of investigation to the problem of improving our personal use and applying his process to the problem of learning how to teach others. Our use improves because we learn to prevent interferences of thought and movement behavior that compromise the integrity and coordination of our system. Using Alexander's process of investigation, we learn how to discipline our thinking to employ his principles as the basis for our patterns of directive guidance in the activities of daily living. We need to learn how to apply these same processes in our efforts to learn how to improve the way in which we teach others.

All of Marjorie Barstow's teaching, all of her innovations, and all of the ways in which she investigates herself, her movement, and Mr. Alexander's ideas lie exactly at the center of the nature and the heart of the work. They always did. For these reasons, it is clear that all of Marjorie's work is absolutely "traditional."

It is only those who have chosen to isolate, preserve, or fossilize certain elements in this work; only those who presume they have reached an endpoint in this work; only those who believe they "know" what is correct and incorrect in human movement and performance; only those who make changes in the structure or manner of their teaching, willy-nilly for the sake of variety, fashion, or profit, without genuine concern for the integrity of the work itself – it is only such people and such programs as these that have earned the title "non-traditional" because they have lost their sense of the true nature of Alexander and his work.

*   *   *   *   *

The essence of this work is improvement, not arrival.

All that Alexander promised us was that if we do what he did; we will experience a constant improvement in the standard of our general performance. Regardless of our level of accomplishment, if we follow Alexander's process of investigation and his procedures, we will always improve in our standard level of performance.

We will still have good days and experiences. We will still have bad ones. But, the average quality of our performance will constantly improve.

Always.

There is no destination on this journey we have all undertaken. There is no condition to attain. No final or superior knowledge to be gained. There is merely a process of investigation and change we may choose to employ.

We all have an understanding about this work based on our study and experience. It is not surprising that we all see just a part of a still-developing picture. I believe that it is important that we stay with methods and concepts that have been proven. But, I also think it is important that we experiment. I think it is essential that we work hard to expand our knowledge of who we are and how we work and how we teach this work.

I do not believe that we are anywhere near the endpoint of the new field of enquiry which Mr. Alexander introduced. I do not believe we have even approached such a condition. I believe we are, at best, deep within the glimmering beginnings of the work that Alexander foretold. Therefore I believe it is our duty, our task, to seek further to clarify the ideas and simplify the procedures involved in the work and teaching it.

We must seek to understand and build upon what has gone before, but we must never hesitate to carry on. We must see our teachers not as individuals who have held or withheld a completed secret, but as individuals who have dared to challenge what they thought and believed and saw, and who carried out experiments in life and process with a willingness to change.

We, too, must be willing to change.

We, too, must be willing to grow as our experience informs us.

We must respect the past. We must learn from it. But, we must also be willing to go on beyond the ideas and procedures of the past: as long as our new ideas are consistent with Alexander's principles, as long as we test and prove our new procedures, and as long as we have a darn good reason to change.

THE INTRODUCTORY CLASS CHARTS

ONE THOUGHT:

the poise of a person's head
in relation with his or her body
in movement
is the key
to freedom
and ease of motion

ALEXANDER'S TWO DISCOVERIES:

All of Alexander's work can be stated in two basic discoveries.

1. In every movement you make, there is a change in the relationship of your
    head with your body that precedes and accompanies that movement, and
    which either helps you or gets in your way.

    In other words, in every movement there are two kinds of movements:

    i.   organizing movements, performed primarily by the axial structures,
         which EITHER create a flexible condition that improves the coordina-
         tion of the movement OR which create an overstretched fixture or a gen-
         eral collapse that lowers the coordination of the movement, and

    ii. task-specific movements which are made up of changes in the angles of
         the joints in the functional regions of the body and which define the ac-
         tual movement itself.

2. The conscious mind has the capacity to override every system, including the
    natural ones.

    In other words, the conscious mind has the power to give us control of our
    own potentialities or to prevent us forever from becoming all that we can be.

WHAT YOU THINK IS WHAT YOU GET

THE MONKEY TRAP

The Problem.

1. There is a nut in a bottle.
2. A monkey sees the nut.
3. The monkey grabs the nut.
4. With the nut in his hand, the monkey can't get his hand out.

Other Solutions.

1. Shake the nut out of the bottle.
2. Break the bottle.
3. Get the nut out with chewing gum on the end of a stick.
4. Break the nut in the bottle, take out the little pieces.
5. Get another nut.

When the monkey sees the nut in the bottle, he reaches in to get it as he has gotten every other nut in the past. He is acting out a typical stimulus-response pattern for monkeys. Because the opening of the bottle is small, the monkey can just barely squeeze his hand in. Because his fist is larger and less flexible with the nut in it, he can't get his hand out and, hence, he is trapped. In the Alexander Technique, we would say the monkey was End-gaining.

End-gaining is the name we give to the process of carrying out an activity with a direct approach and your attention focused on the end you wish to gain, rather than on the manner in which you will gain it.

When we are thinking up other solutions to the problem of getting a nut, we are using an indirect approach to focus on reasoning out the *means* the monkey will use to get the nut. In the Alexander Technique, we would say that our attention is on our Means-whereby.

Frank Jones has written that most people are caught in monkey traps of unconscious habit.

A SOLUTION TO THE "9 DOT" PROBLEM

Shown below is a solution to the problem posed in the chapter on "The Monkey Trap." There is no way to solve this problem without going "outside the lines" one imagines to be there and which make up the "box" most people perceive when they look at this problem. The point to the whole puzzle is to demonstrate that there really are no "lines" to go outside of. There really is no "box". The nine dots are only perceived as making up a "box" because that is an easy convention to use in organizing the nine points in our minds. The problem with this perception is that when we let the easy and familiar convention of thinking of these nine dots as a "box", we are prevented from solving the puzzle by creating a self-imposed limitation that really isn't there.

When I first encountered this problem, I couldn't solve it. I conceived of the dots as making a "box". I not only couldn't conceive of moving outside the "lines" of the "box," but I was sure my classmates had cheated when they went outside the "box" to solve the problem. Since that time, I have become quite adept at looking for solutions outside the "box" in almost all of my problems.

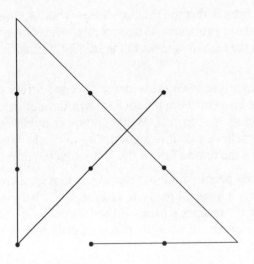

THE BOX CHART FOR BEGINNERS

Part 1:

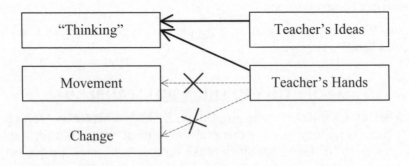

**Thinking, Movement, and Change
in Relation to the Teacher's Ideas
and the Use of the Teacher's Hands**

In everyone, thinking leads to movement and movement leads to change. If there has been a volitional movement, there has been a thought that precedes, plans, and directs that movement.

Change occurs as a result of movement. Many students in this work try to change before they move, in order to move more easily, but this cannot happen. You must move to change. Hence, movement leads to change.

Everyone understands that the teacher's ideas would be used to make changes in a student's thinking processes. Consequently, everyone understands that the arrow drawn from the teacher's ideas to the student's thinking indicates this kind of transaction.

In a similar way, students want to draw a second arrow (shown on the diagram as the upper broken line with an X drawn through it) from the teacher's hands to the student's movements. While I think it might be possible to teach this way, I do not believe that it is a good way to teach, or even a way that we should teach. That's the reason I draw the X through the broken arrow.

In addition, some people think of teaching as though there was an arrow going from the teacher's hands directly to change. They believe that, "somehow," the intervention of the teacher's hands is the instrument of "change" rather than having the change occur as a result of movements that the student makes or stops making as a result of changes in the student's thinking. Because there is no need for this kind of "magical" teaching in this work, this concept is also represented by a broken arrow with an X drawn through it.

I believe that the only transaction we should be performing with our hands in the teaching of this work would be best represented by the unbroken arrow that connects the teacher's hands with the students thinking. I believe that the teacher's hands should only be used to augment or oppose the student's thinking and the only effective point of attack in teaching is the thinking that precedes and directs the movement and not the movement itself.

Therefore, whenever I use my hands with a student, all that I am doing is everything I can to bring about a constructive change in the student's mental processes. In this regard, the physical changes are merely the by-products of the redirection of the student's thinking, and, hence, are incidental to it. Therefore the transactional arrow on the chart goes from the teacher's hands to the student's thinking, not to the student's movement.

Part 2:

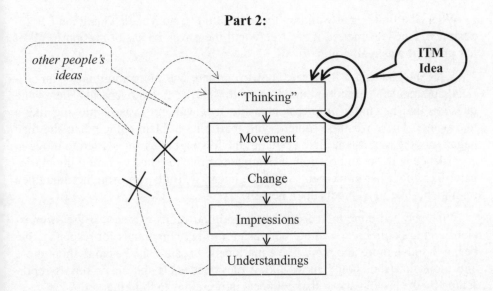

Because our static position recognition receptors can only fire when there has been sufficient movement for them to reach their firing thresholds, and because movement leads to change, it is the movement changes registered by our receptors that lead to impressions. I choose to use the word "impressions" here rather than "feelings" because it is really our impressions that are important to us.

As I have shown earlier, in the absence of organic or disease deficits, there is more feeling sense data generated every second than we can accommodate. We would probably be correct in saying that, for every movement we make, there is a complete set of data transmitted by which we could appreciate every aspect of the movement. It would also probably drive us crazy to be in touch with all of this information.

What is important to us is the small number of bits of information that get through our filters up to the level of the mechanism where these information bits are turned into impressions. We have complete feedback data available almost all of the time, but only a small part of this information is ever processed as impressions. In fact, it is quite common in a lesson for a student to report that they feel "nothing." One student even told me that once, during her first significant Alexander experience, everything below her jaw line disappeared!

The problem with these feeling sense impressions is that we are so accustomed to paying attention to them as a form of guidance that we try to adapt these impressions into the way in which we "do the Alexander Technique."

The most striking example of this occurred once in Nebraska, when a student was asked what she noticed while walking during a lesson. "Oh, I see," she said, "I feel just like a marionette!"

When she first began walking, there was quite a noticeable change in her appearance. Her legs moved more freely and there was an easier motion in all of her joints. It was really quite lovely.

After she had said, "Oh, I see," however, there was more and more of an artificial and mechanical motion imposed on this earlier free movement. There is no question that her initial impression, while first walking, was of moving like a marionette. There was no problem with that. The problem came when she then began moving, not as she first moved in the lesson, but as she started to move in accordance with her impression of being a marionette. There was nothing marionette-like about her movements until she began willfully imposing her imagined marionette-like movements upon herself.

What she had done to accomplish these impositions was to take her impressions and to begin broadcasting them as part of her commands for response. She began to move more and more like a marionette because she began to think more and more that she should move like a marionette. On the chart, this is represented by the broken arrow that connects impressions to thinking.

In other words, once she had gotten a certain impression, she tried to take that impression back up to the top of the chart, and impose that impression on her thinking. This made her begin to move as if she were a marionette, because the commands she was sending out to herself said to move like a marionette. Consequently, what she took away from the lesson was not certain valuable impressions about a new and different way of walking, but a conviction that the right way to walk was like a marionette. Years later, the last time I saw her, these marionette-like movements, which had been unlike any way in which I had ever seen her walk previously before this experience, were still evident in her walking.

In a similar way, some students will be having a lesson and take some idea, or combination of ideas and feeling sense impressions, and have some insight or other. On the chart, this is represented by the box marked "understanding." These kinds of experiences are usually heralded by an exclamation like, "Oh I know what that is!" or "I see what you are trying to say!"

In the same way that our marionette-like friend imposed her feeling sense impressions onto her movement, these students take their "understandings" (the broken line from understanding to thinking) up to the top of the chart, and begin imposing their "understandings" onto their thinking. Because thinking leads to movement, these people will begin moving more and more in accordance with their "understandings," rather than in the way they moved in their lessons that generated their "understanding".

But, this correspondence of subsequent movement and "understandings" is more of a self-fulfilling prophecy than a truth. People move in this new way, not because they are supposed to move in this way, or that this is the way to move, but because they are thinking about moving in this new way, and thinking leads to movement.

The X is drawn through these broken arrows to show to the reader that this is not a good procedure to follow.

The procedure to be followed is for the student to do the "thinking" required. This "thinking" will produce a movement, and the movement will produce a change. While the change will produce feeling sense data every time, there may or may not be an "impression" made on the student. While a student may have many "impressions," they may or may not conceive of any "understanding."

Once the "thinking" has been done and the movement initiated, the rest of the possible results will happen, or they won't. Procedurally, it makes no difference. In almost every case, the procedure to be followed next is that, after having done the "thinking" process required and after having begun to move, the student will go back and do the original "thinking" process again. This, in turn, will generate a second movement and the student will continue to go back to his original "thinking" process again and again and again and again.

On the chart, this cyclic return to the process of "thinking" required to make changes in the use of oneself in activity is represented by the unbroken line which circles from a person's "thinking" back to the original "thinking" process again and again.

ABOUT THE AUTHOR

Donald L. Weed, D.C. studied the Alexander Technique with Marjorie Barstow[161] from 1971 to 1993. He has also studied with other teachers trained by F.M. Alexander and his brother A.R., most notably Frank Pierce Jones and Margaret Goldie.

In addition to his background in sports and the martial arts, Don Weed has an extensive background as an actor, singer, director and performance coach. He has undergraduate degrees in Fine Arts and Human Biology as well as a Doctor of Chiropractic degree. Although he has worked as a teacher in various fields, his deepest and most enduring passion has been studying Alexander's work and sharing it with others.

He began his professional career as a teacher of the Alexander Technique in 1975 and his practice as a health care practitioner in 1982. Professional practice in both areas has enhanced his understanding and skills in each and led to the creation of his own neuro-muscular rehabilitation therapy called "Restructuring".

Since 1975 he has taught Alexander's work to thousands of students around the world. He is the creator of the Interactive Teaching Method for the teaching of the F.M. Alexander Technique (ITM), and has trained Alexander teachers in the Interactive Teaching Method in Switzerland, Germany and the UK.

He currently resides in Switzerland.

---

[161] Marjorie Barstow of Lincoln, Nebraska, was the first person to graduate from F.M. Alexander's first teacher training course for teachers in London in 1933. She later taught as A.R.'s assistant for many years in Boston. In her later years, Ms. Barstow pioneered a groundbreaking approach to teaching the Alexander Technique to groups.